Bob Miller's
PRECALC
HELPER

ROBERT MILLER

Mathematics Department
City College of New York

McGraw-Hill, Inc.
New York St. Louis San Francisco Auckland Bogotá
Caracas Lisbon London Madrid Mexico City Milan
Montreal New Delhi San Juan Singapore
Sydney Tokyo Toronto

To my wonderful wife Marlene:
I dedicate this book
as well as everything else I do in my life to you.
I love you very, very much.

Bob Miller's Precalc Helper

Copyright © 1991 by McGraw-Hill, Inc. All rights reserved. Printed in the United States of America. Except as permitted under the Copyright Act of 1976, no part of this publication may be reproduced or distributed in any form or by any means, or stored in a data base or retrieval system, without the prior written permission of the publisher.

6 7 8 9 10 11 12 13 14 15 16 17 18 19 20 BAW BAW 9 8 7 6 5

ISBN 0-07-042256-7

Sponsoring Editor, David Beckwith
Production Supervisor, Anita Kann
Editing Supervisors, Meg Tobin, Maureen Walker, Patty Andrews
Designer, Wanda Siedlecka
Chapter opener drawing by Leslie Cober;
Cover photo by Zygmunt Malinowski.

Library of Congress Cataloging-in-Publication Data

Miller, Robert A.
    Bob Miller's precalc helper / Robert Miller.
        p.   cm.
    ISBN 0-07-042256-7
    1. Algebra.   2. Trigonometry.   3. Functions.   I. Title.
QA154.2.M56   1991
512'.1 -- dc20   90-13267
                                                                      CIP

ABOUT BOB MILLER . . . IN HIS OWN WORDS.

I received my B.S. and M.S. in math from Brooklyn Poly (now Polytechnic Institute of New York). After teaching my first class there as a substitute for a full professor, one student, upon leaving the room, told another that at least now we have someone who could teach the stuff. I was forever hooked on teaching. Since then I have taught at Westfield State College, Westfield, Massachusetts, Rutgers, and the City College of New York where I've been forever (actually 22 1/2 years). No matter how badly I feel, I always feel great after I start teaching. I especially love to teach precalc and calc courses and am always delighted when a student tells me that he or she has always hated math before and never could learn it but taking a class with me has made math understandable and even enjoyable. I've got a wonderful wife and two great children. I enjoy golf, bowling, bridge, and crossword puzzles, but to me teaching is the greatest joy in the world.

TO THE STUDENT

This book was written for you: not your teacher, not your next-door neighbor, not for anyone but you. I have tried to make the examples and explanations as clear as I can. However, as much as I hate to admit it, I am not perfect. If you find something that is unclear or should be added to this book, please let me know. If you want a response, or I can help you, your class, or your school, in any precalculus or calculus subject, please let me know, but address your comments c/o McGraw-Hill, Inc., Schaum Division, 37th floor, 1221 Avenue of the Americas, New York, N.Y. 10020.

If you make a suggestion on how to teach one of these topics better and you are the first and I use it, I will give you credit for it in the next edition.

Please be patient on responses. I am hoping the book is so good that millions of you will write. I will answer.

Now, enjoy the book and learn.

ROBERT MILLER

CONTENTS

1 LINES, THE STRAIGHT KIND   1

Standard Form   1

2 QUADRATIC EQUATIONS   7

Solving a Quadratic (or higher) by Factoring   7
Quadratic Formula   8

3 INEQUALITIES, LINEAR AND QUADRATIC   11

Linear Inequalities   11
Quadratic Inequalities   12

4 ABSOLUTE VALUE   17

5 EXPONENTS—NEGATIVE, FRACTIONAL   19

6 GEOMETRIC FORMULAS AND FACTS YOU MUST KNOW   22

Circle   23

7 DISTANCE FORMULA, MIDPOINT, CIRCLES, AND PARABOLAS   25

Parabola   26

8 FUNCTIONS   28

Functional Notation   28

9   COMPOSITE AND INVERSE FUNCTIONS   35

Composite Functions   35
Inverse Functions   36

10   TRIGONOMETRY   39

Angles   39
Basic Definitions   40
Multiples of 30°, 45°, 60°, 90°   41
Curve Sketching   43
Identities   47
Attacking Identities   48
Trig Equations   50
Domain and Range of the Trig Functions   53
Double Angles, Half Angles, Sum of 2 Angles, Difference
    of 2 Angles   54
Inverse Trig Functions   59
Right-Angle Trig   61
The Law of Sines   62
Two Angles and a Side   63
Two Sides and an Angle Opposite One of Those Sides   63
The Law of Cosines   64

11   CURVE SKETCHING   65

Polynomials   65
Rational Functions   68
Vertical Asymptotes   68
Horizontal Asymptotes   69

12   MODERN LOGARITHMS   75

13   PARABOLAS II, ELLIPSES, AND HYPERBOLAS   81

14   WRITING FUNCTIONS OF x, THE ALGEBRAIC PART OF CALCULUS WORD PROBLEMS   91

15   THE BINOMIAL THEOREM   100

ACKNOWLEDGMENTS   103

INDEX   105

1. LINES, THE STRAIGHT KIND

In elementary algebra, you learned how to graph points and how to graph lines. We will briefly review graphing and then attack the harder problem, finding the equation of a straight line.

Standard form

When we look at an equation, we should instantly know that it is a straight line. Any equation in the form $Ax + By = C$, where A,B,C are numbers and A and B are not both equal to zero. (**Note:** In some books, standard form is $Ax + By + C = 0$, so standard form isn't standard. Isn't that funny?!) Let us make sure we understand this by giving some examples that are straight lines and some that are not.

EXAMPLE(S) 1

   a. $3x - 4y = 7$ b. $5x = 9$ c. $x/3 - y/7 = 7$

   d. $3/x + 5/y = 9$ e. $xy = 7$ f. $x^2 - 3y = 5$

     Note: a,b,c, are lines. Coefficients may be negative or fractions or, as in b, $B = 0$. d is not a straight line since the letters are in the bottom. e is not a straight line since the variables are multiplied. f is not a straight line since the exponents of each letter must be 1.

Definition   SLOPE — The slope (or slant) of a line is defined by $m = (y_2 - y_1)/(x_2 - x_1)$.

Notes: 1.   The letter m is always used for the slope.

2. The 1's and 2's are subscripts, standing for point 1 and point 2. The 1 and the 2 mean x_1, x_2, y_1, y_2 stand for numbers, not variables, but we are not telling you what they are yet.

3. The calculus notation is $m = \Delta y / \Delta x$, where Δ is the Greek letter delta, and means the change in y over the change in x.

4. The y's are always on top.

EXAMPLE(S) 2 ON THE SLOPE. We will graph the line that joins the points after this example and discuss further. Find the slope between

A. (2,3) and (6,12)

B. (4,−3) and (−1,3)

C. (1,3) and (6,3)

D. (2,5) and (2,8)

EXAMPLE 2 SOLUTIONS

2A. $(2, 3)$ and $(6, 12)$

    ↑ ↑   ↑ ↑

    $x_1 \, y_1$ $x_2 \, y_2$ $m = \dfrac{y_2 - y_1}{x_2 - x_1} = \dfrac{12 - 3}{6 - 2} = 9/4$

Note: Until you get good at this, label the points just like I did. Also it does not matter which is point 1 and which is point 2.

2B. $(4, -3)$ and $(-1, 3)$

    ↑ ↑   ↑ ↑

    $x_1 \, y_1$ $x_2 \, y_2$ $m = \dfrac{y_2 - y_1}{x_2 - x_1} = \dfrac{3 - (-3)}{-1 - 4} = 6/-5$

Note: In $3 - (-3)$, the first minus sign is the $-$ in the equation, and the second comes from the fact that y_1 is negative. BE CAREFUL!

2C. (1,3) and (6,3) $m = (3 - 3)/6 - 1) = 0/5 = 0$

2D. (2,5) and (2,8) $m = (8 - 5)/(2 - 2) = 3/0$ — undefined, no slope, or infinite slope

2A. If you walk in the direction of the arrow, when you get to the line and have to walk up, you always have a POSITIVE SLOPE.

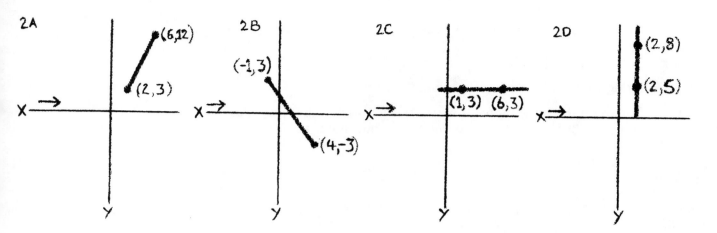

2B. If you have to walk down, you have a NEGATIVE SLOPE.

2C. Horizontal lines have m = 0.

2D. Vertical lines have no slope or infinite slope.

Definition INTERCEPTS — X-INTERCEPT, where the line hits the x-axis, is where y = 0. Y-INTERCEPT is where x = 0.

EXAMPLE 3 Given $3x - 4y = 12$. Find the intercepts and graph the line.

x-intercept y = 0. 3x = 12. x = 4. The point is (4,0). (x coord. is always first.)

y-intercept x = 0. −4y = 12. y = −3. The point is (0,−3), and the graph is as shown.

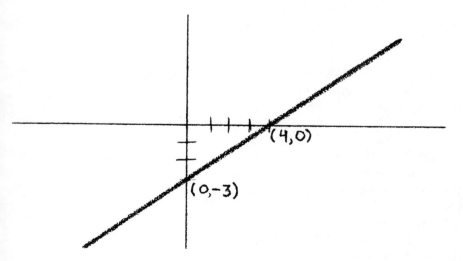

Note: This is the easiest way to graph a line with 2 intercepts.

There are 3 exceptions, the ones with only 1 intercept:

$x = 3$ (all vertical lines are $x = $ something)

$y = 5$ (all horizontal lines are $y = $ something)

$y = 3x$ [where the only intercept is $(0,0)$]. Pick some other point, say take $x = 2$. So $y = 6$ and we get the second point $(2,6)$.

Graphs are all included in the picture here.

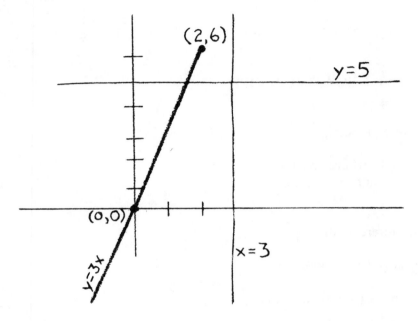

We are almost ready to find the equation of a line. There are 4 basic forms of a line. The 2 main ones are the point-slope and the slope-intercept.

Definition   SLOPE-INTERCEPT — $y = mx + b$.   When you solve for y, the co-efficient of x is the slope. b is the y-intercept—when $x = 0$, $y = b$. This is the most common form in high school books.

Definition   POINT-SLOPE — $m = (y - y_1)/(x - x_1)$.   You are given the slope and a point (x_1, y_1). The point-slope is given in different forms in different books. I will try to convince you that this form is the best to use because it eliminates much of the arithmetic fractions, which tend to bother too many of you.

We will now do some problems of this type. Although they are not long problems, most students have difficulty at first. Don't get discouraged if you do.

EXAMPLE 4   Find the equation of the line through the points $(2,3)$ and $(7,11)$ and write the answer in standard form.

We will do this problem 2 different ways. I think you may be convinced the point-slope method is better.

Point-slope	**Slope-intercept**
(2,3) and (7,11)	**(2,3) and (7,11)**
$m = (11 - 3)/(7 - 2) = 8/5$	$m = (11 - 3)/(7 - 2) = 8/5$
$m = \dfrac{y - y_1}{x - x_1}$	$y = mx + b$
	$y = (8/5)x + b$
	$3 = (8/5)(2) + b$
$\dfrac{8}{5} = \dfrac{y - 3}{x - 2}$	$3 = (16/5) + b$
	$b = 3 - 16/5 = 15/5 - 16/5 = -1/5$
$8(x - 2) = 5(y - 3)$	$y = (8/5)x - 1/5$
$8x - 16 = 5y - 15$	$5y = 8x - 1$
$8x - 5y = 1$	$-8x + 5y = -1$ or
	$8x - 5y = 1$

The reason the point-slope method is easier for most is that the only fractional skill is cross multiplication,* a skill most math students do very well. The slope-intercept method requires a number of fractional skills. About 90% of the time, point-slope is better.

At this stage of your mathematics, all of you should put the lines in standard form to practice your algebra skills. However to save space and keep the book friendlier, I will leave the answer in either of these 2 forms.

EXAMPLE 5 Write the equation of the line with slope 3, y-intercept 7.

$y = mx + b$ is the easiest. $y = 3x + 7$.

EXAMPLE 6 Write the equation of the line with slope -4 and x-intercept 9.

Tricky. $m = -4$ and point $(9,0)$. Use point-slope.

$$m = \frac{y - y_1}{x - x_1} \qquad -4 = \frac{y - 0}{x - 9}$$

EXAMPLE 7 A. Find the equation of the line parallel to $3x + 4y = 5$ through $(6,7)$. B. Find the equation of the line perpendicular to $3x + 4y = 5$ through $(8,-9)$.

Parallel lines have same slope. Perpendicular lines have negative reciprocal slopes. In either case we must solve for y.

*See the third-to-last line in the preceding point-slope column.

$3x + 4y = 5$. $4y = -3x + 5$. $y = (-3/4)x + 5/4$. We only care about the co-efficient of x, which is the slope. The slope is $-3/4$.

A. Parallel means equal slopes.
    $m = -3/4$, the point is $(6, 7)$
    The equation is

$$-3/4 = \frac{y - 7}{x - 6}$$

B. Perpendicular means the slope is the negative reciprocal.
    $m = +4/3$, the point is $(8, -9)$
    The equation is

$$4/3 = \frac{y - (-9)}{x - 8}$$

or

$$4/3 = \frac{y + 9}{x - 8}$$

2. QUADRATIC EQUATIONS

A topic you should have either partially or totally done before is solve quadratic formulas, but I can't leave this to chance. Let's do it.

Solving a quadratic (or higher) by factoring

Note: If the product of 2 numbers is zero, at least 1 must be zero. In letters, if $(a)(b) = 0$, either $a = 0$ or $b = 0$.

EXAMPLE 1 $(x - 4)(x + 5) = 0$

$x - 4 = 0$ so $x = 4$. $x + 5 = 0$ so $x = -5$. Two answers are 4 and -5.

EXAMPLE 2 $x(x - 4)(x + 7)(2x - 9)(3x + 1) = 0$.

Setting each factor equal to 0, the answers are $x = 0$, 4, -7, 9/2, and $-1/3$.

Practice doing this in your head!!!!! It is not hard if you try.

EXAMPLE 3

$$x^2 - 2x = 8$$ **Get everything on 1 side— arrange terms highest exponent to lowest exponent**

$$x^2 - 2x - 8 = 0$$ **Now factor and set each one equal to 0 as before**

$$(x - 4)(x + 2) = 0$$

So $x = 4$ and -2.

EXAMPLE 4

$$x^3 - 7x^2 - 8x = 0$$ **A cubic—3 solutions**

$$x(x-8)(x+1) = 0$$

So $x = 0, 8, -1$.

EXAMPLE 5

$$(x-2)(x-3) = 2$$ **At first this looks rather tame. However factored form must equal 0. So there is a bit of work to do**

$$x^2 - 5x + 6 = 2$$ **Multiply out, everything to 1 side, and then refactor**

$$x^2 - 5x + 4 = 0$$

$$(x-4)(x-1) = 0$$

The answers are $x = 4$ and 1.

If you are not terrific at factoring, you should PRACTICE, PRACTICE, PRACTICE!!!!!!

QUADRATIC FORMULA

What if the equation does not factor? If it is a quadratic, there is a formula that will work. We will derive it here because you should see it and some teachers actually make students do this (many times) by the method used to prove this formula. We need a brief introduction.

Brief introduction. Get a perfect square. $(x + k)^2 = x^2 + 2kx + k^2$. If the coefficient of x^2 is 1, take half of the coefficient of x (half of 2k, which is k) and square it to get k^2, the sum of which factors into 2 identical terms. $x^2 + 10x$. Half of 10 is 5. 5^2 is 25. $x^2 + 10x + 25 = (x + 5)(x + 5) = (x + 5)^2$.

How about a little more? Suppose we had $x^2 + ax$. Half of a is $\frac{1}{2}a$. Square it—$\frac{1}{4}a^2$. We have $x^2 + ax + \frac{1}{4}a^2 = (x + \frac{1}{2}a)^2$! Now let us get back to our problem.

We will solve the quadratics $3x^2 - 7x - 6 = 0$ and $ax^2 + bx + c = 0$ simultaneously, preceded on the right by what we are doing on the next step.

$$3x^2 - 7x - 6 = 0 \qquad ax^2 + bx + c = 0$$ **Divide by coeff. of x^2**

$$\frac{3x^2}{3} - \frac{7x}{3} - \frac{6}{3} = \frac{0}{3} \qquad \frac{ax^2}{a} + \frac{bx}{a} + \frac{c}{a} = \frac{0}{a}$$ **Get the term without x to the other side**

$$x^2 - \frac{7x}{3} = 2 \qquad x^2 + \frac{bx}{a} = \frac{-c}{a}$$ **Complete the square. Take half the coeff. of x, square it, and add to both sides**

$$x^2 - \frac{7x}{3} + \left(-\frac{7}{6}\right)^2 = \left(-\frac{7}{6}\right)^2 + 2 \qquad x^2 + \frac{bx}{a} + \left(\frac{b}{2a}\right)^2$$

$$= \left(\frac{b}{2a}\right)^2 - c/a$$

Factor left side and do arithmetic and algebra on right side

$$\left(x - \frac{7}{6}\right)^2 = \frac{49}{36} + \frac{72}{36} = \frac{121}{36} \qquad \left(x + \frac{b}{2a}\right)^2 = \frac{b^2}{4a^2} - \frac{c(4a)}{a(4a)}$$

$$= \frac{b^2 - 4ac}{4a^2}$$

Take square root of both sides

$$x - \frac{7}{6} = \pm\frac{11}{6} \qquad\qquad x = \frac{b}{2a} \pm \frac{\sqrt{b^2 - 4ac}}{2a}$$

Isolate x and get the 2 solutions (roots)

$$x = \frac{7}{6} \pm \frac{11}{6} \qquad\qquad x = \frac{-b}{2a} \pm \frac{\sqrt{b^2 - 4ac}}{2a}$$

$$x_1 = \frac{7}{6} + \frac{11}{6} = \frac{18}{6} = 3 \qquad x_1 = \frac{-b + \sqrt{b^2 - 4ac}}{2a}$$

$$x_2 = \frac{7}{6} - \frac{11}{6} = -\frac{4}{6} = -2/3 \qquad x_2 = \frac{-b - \sqrt{b^2 - 4ac}}{2a}$$

The theorem we just proved, the quadratic formula, states that given the equation $ax^2 + bx + c = 0$, with $a \neq 0$, the roots will be $x = (-b \pm \sqrt{b^2 - 4ac})/2a$, where a is the coefficient of the x^2 term, b is the coefficient of the x term, and c is the term without x.

Let us do some examples. The first one we will do is the above example using the quadratic formula.

EXAMPLE 6 Solve $3x^2 - 7x - 6 = 0$ using the quadratic formula. $a = 3$, $b = -7$, $c = -6$.

$$x = \frac{-(-7) \pm \sqrt{(-7)^2 - 4(3)(-6)}}{2(3)}$$

$$x = \frac{7 \pm \sqrt{121}}{6}$$

As before $x = 3$ and $-2/3$.

Note 1: After we proved this formula, look how easy it is to use.

Note 2: This problem can be factored. You should always try to factor first. $3x^2 - 7x - 6 = 0$. $(3x + 2)(x - 3) = 0$. Again $x = 3$, $-2/3$. The main reason for the formula is if the quadratic does NOT factor.

EXAMPLE 7 $2x^2 + 5x + 1 = 0$. $a = 2$, $b = 5$, $c = 1$. Sooooo . . .

$$x = \frac{-5 \pm \sqrt{5^2 - 4(2)(1)}}{2(2)} \qquad x = \frac{-5 \pm \sqrt{17}}{4}$$

This is the major use for this formula.

EXAMPLE 8 $3x^2 + 5x + 7 = 0$. $a = 3$, $b = 5$, $c = 7$.

$$x = \frac{-5 \pm \sqrt{5^2 - 4(3)(7)}}{2(3)} = \frac{-5 \pm \sqrt{-59}}{2(3)} = \frac{-5 \pm i\sqrt{59}}{6}$$

Note: $\sqrt{-1} = i$. $\sqrt{-59} = \sqrt{-1}\sqrt{59} = i\sqrt{59}$. This is in a topic called imaginary (complex) numbers. This is part of some elementary algebra books. If this book is not too long, we will review it here. In any case, basic imaginary-number properties are very easy (all of algebra should be that easy).

Most of you will do very well with this formula. However very few students know it as well as I want my students to know it. Try this little exercise to see if you *really* know what the formula says.

Little exercise.   For each of the following, tell what a is, b is, c is. After you do one, look at the answers before you do the next.

1. $3x^2 - x - 7 = 0$. $a = ?$, $b = ?$, $c = ?$.   2. $7x - x^2 = 0$. $a = ?$, $b = ?$, $c = ?$.

3. $a^2x^2 - bx + c = 0$. $a = ?$, $b = ?$, $c = ?$.   4.   (Really tough) $-x^2 + b^2 + 7 = 0$.

5. $3x^2 + bx + 7x - 5 = 0$. $a = ?$, $b = ?$, $c = ?$.

Answers.   1. $a = 3$, $b = -1$, $c = -7$. 2. $a = -1$, $b = 7$, $c = 0$. 3. $a = a^2$, $b = -b$, $c = c$. 4. $a = -1$, $b = 0$, $c = b^2 + 7$!! 5. $a = 3$, $b = (b + 7)$, $c = -5$.

If you understand the last 5 examples, you really understand the formula.

3. INEQUALITIES, LINEAR AND QUADRATIC

LINEAR INEQUALITIES

Let us review linear inequalities. This is a topic I hope you are familiar with, but just to make sure, we will go over it.

Linear inequalities are done in exactly the same way as linear equalities, except when you multiply or divide by a negative number, the order is reversed. **Note:** $8 < 12$; then $8/2 < 12/2$ since $4 < 6$, but $8/-2 > 12/-2$ since $-4 > -6$.

EXAMPLE 1

$4(3x - 5) - 2(4x - 6) \le 6x - 14$	**Mult. out parentheses**
$12x - 20 - 8x + 12 \le 6x - 14$	**On each side, combine like terms**
$4x - 8 \le 6x - 14$	**Add $-6x$ to each side**
$-2x - 8 \le -14$	**Add $+8$ to each side**
$-2x \le -6$	**Divide each side by -2, order reverses**
$x \ge +3$	

The graph looks like this:

The solid dot means 3 is part of the answer. An open dot would mean it is not.

EXAMPLE 2

$$-3 < 2x - 7 \leq 16$$

We are solving a double inequality. The x must be left in the middle. Add 7 to each term

$$4 < 2x \leq 23$$

Then divide each term by 2

$$2 < x \leq 23/2$$

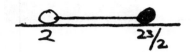

QUADRATIC INEQUALITIES

One of my favorite topics. I think I teach it about as well as anyone. Most books do a rather poor job. I think you'll like this topic after these few pages.

EXAMPLE 3

$$x^2 - 7x > 8$$

Get everything to 1 side, coefficient of x^2 positive, and then factor (in some examples you might need the quadratic formula)

$$x^2 - 7x - 8 > 0$$

$$(x - 8)(x + 1) > 0$$

Draw a graph with an open dot on 8 and an open dot on -1. We are solving the equality $(x - 8)(x + 1) = 0$, so $x = 8, -1$ doesn't solve given inequality

There are 3 regions on the graph—$x > 8$, $-1 < x < 8$, and $x < -1$. The technique is to substitute a number in each of the regions, but DO NOT DO THE ARITHMETIC since we only care about the SIGN of the answer.

1. Take a number bigger than 8, say 10. Substitute in $(x - 8)(x + 1) > 0$. $10 - 8$ is positive, $10 + 1$ is positive, and the product is positive, which is greater than 0, so the region $x > 8$ IS part of the answer.

2. Take a number between -1 and 8, say 3. $3 - 8$ is neg and $3 + 1$ is pos, and the product is neg, which is NOT greater than 0. $-1 < x < 8$ is not part of the answer.

3. Take a number less than -1, say -100. $-100 - 8$ is neg and $-100 + 1$ is neg, and the product is pos, which IS greater than 0, so $x < -1$ is part of the answer.

The graph looks like this:

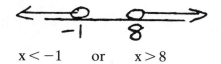

$$x < -1 \quad \text{or} \quad x > 8$$

Note: Once you do a few of these, this technique is *very* easy. We will do a number more.

EXAMPLE 4 $(x - 2)(x - 4)(x - 6)(x - 8) \leq 0$

With other techniques this problem would take a very long time, but after we finish this example, this will take you 10 seconds.

Solution: Solid dot on 2,4,6,8, since product can equal 0.

Substitute $x = 9$. $(9 - 2)(9 - 4)(9 - 6)(9 - 8)$ is the product of all positive terms, so product couldn't be negative or zero, so $x > 8$ is not part of the answer.

$x = 7$. All terms pos except $7 - 8$. Whole product is neg. $6 \leq x \leq 8$ part of answer.

$x = 5$. Two neg terms $(5 - 8)(7 - 8)$. Product positive. $4 < x < 6$ not part of the answer.

$x = 3$. Three negative terms. $2 \leq x \leq 4$ is part of the answer.

$x = 1$. Four negative terms. $x < 2$ is not part of the answer.

So the total answer is $2 \leq x \leq 4$ or $6 \leq x \leq 8$ and the graph is

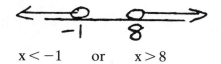

The next problem is even easier. If all the exponents are 1 (or odd numbers), every other region is part of the answer. So if $x > 8$ is no, then $6 \leq x \leq 8$ must be yes, $4 < x < 6$ is no, $2 \leq x \leq 4$ is yes, and $x < 2$ is no!!!!!!! Easy, huh?!!!!!!

EXAMPLE 5 $\dfrac{(x - 1)(x - 3)(x - 5)}{(x - 7)(x - 9)} \geq 0$

Look how easy. Solid dot on 1,3,5 since the top of the fraction can equal 0. Open dot on 7,9 since the bottom of a fraction can never be 0.

All we need is to substitute 1 number—x = 10. Since everything is positive, the product is positive and $x > 9$ is part of the answer. Since all the exponents are odd, every other region is part of the answer. $7 \le x \le 9$ is not, $5 \le x < 7$ is, $3 < x < 5$ is not, $1 \le x \le 3$ is, and $x < 1$ is not.

The solution is $x > 9$ or $5 \le x < 7$ or $1 \le x \le 3$. The graph is

Note: In doing these problems graph the points, here 1,3,5,7,9, with appropriate open or closed dots first, determine the regions next, and lastly write the algebraic solutions.

EXAMPLE 6 $\dfrac{2x - 5}{x - 3} > 1$

$$\frac{2x - 5}{x - 3} - 1 > 0 \quad \text{or} \quad \frac{2x - 5}{x - 3} - \frac{x - 3}{x - 3} = \frac{x - 2}{x - 3} > 0$$

Substituting x = 5 and noting it *is* part of the answer, and that all the exponents are 1 so every other region is the answer, the algebraic answer is $x > 3$ or $x < 2$ and its graph is

$$\xleftarrow{\hspace{1cm}} \underset{2}{\circ} \quad \underset{3}{\circ} \xrightarrow{\hspace{1cm}}$$

EXAMPLE 7

$$\frac{2x - 6}{x - 3} \le \frac{x - 2}{x - 3}$$

Since both bottoms are the same, get everything to the side where the coefficient of the top is going to be positive and subtract the fractions

$$\frac{2x - 6}{x - 3} - \frac{x - 2}{x - 3} = \frac{x - 4}{x - 3} \le 0$$

We proceed as before: solid dot on 4 and an open dot on 3. Substitute a number bigger than the rightmost point (4), say x = 6. We get $(6 - 4)/(6 - 3)$, which is certainly not less than or equal to 0. So the right end is not part of the answer. Since all exponents are odd, every other region is part of the answer. In this case only the middle is the answer: $3 < x \le 4$. Its graph is

Solid dot on H since the top can = 0
Open dot on 3 since the bottom can never be 0

$$\xrightarrow{\hspace{0.5cm}} \underset{3}{\circ}\!\!-\!\!\underset{4}{\bullet} \rule{1cm}{0.4pt}$$

EXAMPLE 8

$$\frac{x-3}{x-1} > \frac{x-5}{x-2}$$

$$\frac{x-3}{x-1} > \frac{x-5}{x-2} \quad \text{or} \quad \frac{x-3}{x-1} - \frac{x-5}{x-2} = \frac{(x-3)(x-2)-(x-5)(x-1)}{(x-1)(x-2)}$$

$$= \frac{(x+1)}{(x-1)(x-2)} > 0$$

Only the algebra is messier. Getting all the terms to 1 side, you should subtract the fractions by sight. Note:

$$\frac{a}{b} - \frac{c}{d} = \frac{ad-bc}{bd}.$$ **With a little practice you can do this easily!!!**

We proceed as before: open dot on $-1,1,2$. Substitute a number to the right of 2, say $x = 5$. Everything is positive so that $x > 2$ is part of the answer. Again all exponents are odd so every other region is part of the answer. The answer is $x > 2$ or $-1 < x < 1$, and its graph is

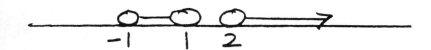

EXAMPLE 9

$$\frac{(x^2+15)(x-2)^3(x-4)^4(x-6)^5}{(x-8)^6} \geq 0$$

Now don't panic. This is a LOT easier than it looks, especially if you did the previous examples. First note that no matter what x is, $x^2 + 15$ is always positive. In an inequality it means you can discount it. So throw it out!! The problem is now

$$\frac{(x-2)^3(x-4)^4(x-6)^5}{(x-8)^6} \geq 0$$

Not much better yet. However it really is easy. Solid dot on 2,4,6 and open dot on 8 as before.

Substitute $x = 9$. All terms positive—$x > 8$ is part of the answer.

$x = 7$. All terms positive—$6 \leq x < 8$ is also part of the answer.

$x = 5$. One term negative $(5-6)^5$, so expression is negative—$4 < x < 6$ not part of answer.

$x = 3$. Same 1 term negative, so $2 < x < 4$ is not part of the answer.

$x = 1$. Two terms negative, product is positive—$x \leq 2$ is part of the answer.

The answer is $x \leq 2$ or $x = 4$ or $6 \leq x < 8$ or $x > 8$. Its graph looks like this:

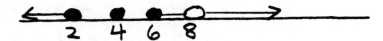

Note: There are several weird things that happen here: $x > 8$ is part of the answer and $6 \leq x < 8$ is part of the answer, but $x = 8$ is not part of the answer; $x = 4$ is part of the answer, but the region to the left and the region to the right are not part of the answer. We have an isolated point. Lots of fun things are possible, when exponents are both even and odd. But with a little practice, all these problems should be easy.

4. ABSOLUTE VALUE

There are 2 definitions of absolute value. We will give both since both are used.

Definition 1   ABSOLUTE VALUE — $|x| = x$ if $x > 0$
$$= -x \text{ if } x < 0$$
$$= 0 \text{ if } x = 0$$

Using numbers, $|9| = 9$, since $9 > 0$; $|-3| = -(-3) = 3$, since $-3 < 0$; and $|0| = 0$.

Definition 2   ABSOLUTE VALUE — $|x| = \sqrt{x^2}$; that is, $|-6| = \sqrt{(-6)^2} = \sqrt{36} = 6$.

You might say the second definition is much easier, and you would be correct. However, the first definition is almost always easier to use, as we will see, and in some cases the second definition is virtually unusable.

Let us list some properties of absolute value. They all can be verified by substituting numbers.

Property 1: $|ab| = |a|\,|b|$.

Property 2: $|a/b| = |a|/|b|$, if $b \neq 0$.

Property 3: $|a - b| = |b - a|$.

Property 4:   The triangle inequality $|a + b| \leq |a| + |b|$.

The last property is most interesting and is used later in your math. If a is 0, or if a and b are both positive, or if a and b are both negative, the statement is an equality. However if, let us say, $a = 6$ and $b = -2$, it is an inequality. You might ask, "Why the heck do I want an inequality?" There are 2 reasons: (1) that is all you can get; (2) if we can show $x \leq y$ AND $y \leq x$, we get $x = y$! Pretty sneaky, eh? However this is for later. But it is important to preview it now so that later this will not be scary.

17

We are now ready to do the absolute value problems.

EXAMPLE 1 $|x - 4| = 6$

Using definition 1, $x - 4 = 6$ or $x - 4 = -6$, since the absolute value of 6 and -6 is 6. The answers are $x = 10$ and $x = -2$.

Let us show how messy it is to use the other definition.

$$(x - 4)^2 = 6^2 \quad \text{or} \quad (x - 4)^2 = 36 \quad \text{or} \quad x^2 - 8x + 16 = 36$$

$$\text{or} \quad x^2 - 8x - 20 = 0$$

Factoring we get $(x - 10)(x + 2) = 0$. Again the answers are 10 and -2 . . . except we have done much more work!!!!

EXAMPLE 2 $|3x - 7| = 0$. Only 1 solution—$3x - 7 = 0$ or $x = 7/3$.

EXAMPLE 3 $|4x + 7| = -5$. No solution, since the absolute value is never negative.

EXAMPLE 4 $|x - 8| < 3$

To give you an idea of what this means, we will use a picture. The absolute value can stand for the distance between 2 points. The example says we are looking for all points x that differ from 8 by less than 3. Here is the picture:

Note: "Outsides" are greater than picture. Algebraically, $-3 < x - 8 < 3$ or $5 < x < 11$.

EXAMPLE 5 $|8x - 4| < -9$. No solution since the absolute value is never negative.

EXAMPLE 6 $|5 - 4x| \geq 6$

Since I don't like the way it looks, property 3 allows me to write it as $|4x - 5| \geq 6$. There are 2 parts: $4x - 5 \geq 6$ or $4x - 5 \leq -6$. The solution is $x \geq 11/4$ or $x \leq -\frac{1}{4}$. Its graph looks like this:

EXAMPLE 7 $|2x - 5| \geq -3$. The solution is all real numbers since the absolute value is always bigger than a negative number.

5. EXPONENTS—NEGATIVE, FRACTIONAL

One of the easiest yet most forgettable topics concerns exponents. We will try to do all the new stuff and, at the same time, go over problems from the past.

Definition   NEGATIVE EXPONENTS — $a^{-n} = 1/a^n$, $b^{-3} = 1/b^3$, and $1/m^{-4} = m^4$. In other words, "negative exponent" means reciprocal and has nothing to do with negative numbers!

EXAMPLES 1 and 2 $5^{-2} = 1/5^2 = 1/25$. $(-4)^{-3} = 1/(-4)^3 = 1/-64 = -1/64$.

Definition   FRACTIONAL EXPONENTS — $a^{p/r}$, where p is the power and r is the root.

Always do the root first!!!

EXAMPLE 3 $27^{2/3} = (\sqrt[3]{27})^2 = 3^2 = 9$

EXAMPLE 4 $16^{-(3/2)} = 1/16^{3/2} = 1/(\sqrt{16})^3 = 1/4^3 = 1/64$

Rule 1 $a^m a^n = a^{m+n}$. If the bases are the same, when you multiply, you add the exponents, and leave the base unchanged.

EXAMPLE 5 $(5a^{2/3})(4a^{3/2}) = 20a^{2/3+3/2} = 20a^{13/6}$

Remember—coefficients are multiplied; exponents are added.

Rule 2 $(a^m)^n = a^{mn}$. Power to a power, you multiply exponents.

EXAMPLE 6 $(4a^{5/7})^{3/2} = 4^{3/2}a^{15/14} = 8a^{15/14}$
Don't forget the numerical coefficient!

Rule 3 $a^m/a^n = a^{m-n}$ or $1/a^{n-m}$. If the bases are the same, "divide" means subtract the exponents, leaving the base the same.

EXAMPLE 7 $\dfrac{a^6b^{-3}c^{-7}}{a^{-9}b^4c^{-5}} = \dfrac{a^6a^9c^5}{b^3b^4c^7} = \dfrac{a^{15}}{b^7c^2}$

Note: If the problem contains only multiplication and division, negative exponents in the top become positive exponents in the bottom, and negative exponents in the bottom become positive exponents in the top.

Rule 4 $(ab)^n = a^nb^n$

EXAMPLE 8 $(a^4b^{-3})^{-2} = a^{-8}b^6 = b^6/a^8$

Rule 5 $(a/b)^n = a^n/b^n$

EXAMPLE 9 $(3a^4/b^{-5})^{-3} = 3^{-3}a^{-12}/b^{15} = 1/27a^{12}b^{15}$

EXAMPLE 10 $(a^4b^{-9}/b^{-5}a^{-3})^{-2} = (a^4b^5a^3/b^9)^{-2} = (a^7/b^4)^{-2}$
$= (b^4/a^7)^2 = b^8/a^{14}$

EXAMPLE 11

$\dfrac{a^{-2}-b^{-2}}{a^{-1}-b^{-1}}$

The problem is harder because of the subtraction. It is also a favorite of mine since it contains a number of skills in a relatively short problem

$$\dfrac{a^{-2}-b^{-2}}{a^{-1}-b^{-1}} = \dfrac{\dfrac{1}{a^2} - \dfrac{1}{b^2}}{\dfrac{1}{a} - \dfrac{1}{b}}$$

Definition of negative exponent

$$= \dfrac{\dfrac{1}{a^2}\dfrac{a^2b^2}{1} - \dfrac{1}{b^2}\dfrac{a^2b^2}{1}}{\dfrac{1}{a}\dfrac{a^2b^2}{1} - \dfrac{1}{b}\dfrac{a^2b^2}{1}}$$

This is a small review of complex fractions. Find the LCD of all the fractions, multiply each fraction top and bottom by the LCD

$$= \frac{b^2 - a^2}{ab^2 - ba^2}$$ **Multiply and simplify each fraction**

$$= \frac{(b-a)(b+a)}{ab(b-a)} = \frac{b+a}{ab}$$ **Factor and cancel**

At this point, I usually give my classes 2 short, non-counting quizzes to see if they really know the laws. You might try them.

Quiz 1 1. $(4a^3)(3a^4)$. 2. $4a^3 + 3a^4$. 3. $(4a^3)(4a^3)$. 4. $4a^3 + 4a^3$.
5. $(4a^3)^3$.

The purpose of the quiz is to see if you know the difference between the adding and multiplying rules.

1. Multiplying. Multiply coefficients, add exponents. Answer is $12a^7$.

2. Adding. We can only add like terms—these are unlike. Answer is $4a^3 + 3a^4$.

3. Multiplying. $16a^6$.

4. Adding. Like terms—add coefficients, *leave exponents alone*. $8a^3$.

5. Rule 2. $64a^9$.

The second quiz is even harder. Try it.

Quiz 2 1. $4^7 4^{11}$. 2. $b^{2x+3} b^{4x+7}$. 3. $(a^{4x+3})(a^{7x})/a^c$ (only one a in the answer). 4. $2^n + 2^n$. 5. $3^n + 3^n$. 6. $3^n + 3^n + 3^n$.

1. Multiplying. Add exponents, but the base stays the same. 4^{18}.

2. Same as 1. b^{6x+10}.

3. Same as 1 plus if you divide, you subtract exponents. $a^{11x+3-c}$.

4. Very tough adding problem. When you add, you add the coefficients, leaving the base alone—coefficient is 1!!! Second part: Base the same (mult.) add, exponents. $2^n + 2^n = (1)2^n + (1)2^n = 2(2^n) = 2^1 2^n = 2^{n+1}$.

5. $3^n + 3^n = 1(3^n) + 1(3^n) = 2(3^n)$—answer, since bases are different, but . . . .

6. $3^n + 3^n + 3^n = 3(3^n) = 3^1 3^n = 3^{n+1}$!!!!!

If you know all of these, then you really know your exponents!!!!!!!!

6. GEOMETRIC FORMULAS AND FACTS YOU MUST KNOW

This chapter contains a list of geometric formulas and facts that it is hoped you know very, very well. Some are needed for precalc, some are needed for trig, and all are needed for calculus.

Area $A = bh$ (base times height). Perimeter $p = 2b + 2h$. (In case you forget the formula, perimeter means "to add up all the sides.") Diagonal $d = \sqrt{b^2 + h^2}$.

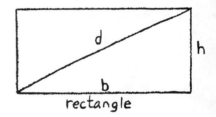
rectangle

$A = s^2$ (side squared). $p = 4s$. $d = s\sqrt{2}$.

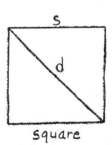
square

Volume $V = \ell wh$ (length times width times height). $d = (\ell^2 + w^2 + h^2)^{1/2}$.

Surface area $SA = 2\ell w \quad\quad + 2wh + 2\ell h$
$\qquad\qquad$ top, bottom $\quad$ ends $\quad$ back, front

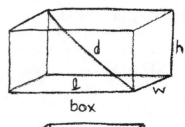
box

$V = e^3$ (edge cubed). $SA = 6e^2$. $d = e\sqrt{3}$.

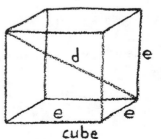
cube

Circle

O = centered circle, OC = radius, r. AB = diameter, d. $r = \frac{1}{2}d$. $A = \pi r^2$ (pi r^2). $c = 2\pi r = \pi d$ (c = circumference—perimeter of circle). DE is a chord. **Note:** The diameter is the largest chord. l_1 = tangent—a line hitting a circle in only 1 point. ℓ_2 = secant—a line hitting a circle in 2 points.

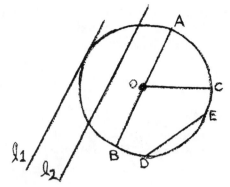

A sector is a part of a circle, like a section of a pie. θ (theta, a Greek letter like pi) usually indicates an angle. s (small s) = arc length, part of the circumference.

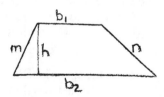

Sector

Angles are measured here in 2 different ways: degrees (like you know) and radians, which we will talk about in the trig chapter. Area $A = (\theta°/360°)\pi r^2$ or $\frac{1}{2}\theta r^2$, where θ is in radians. $s = (\theta°/360°)2\pi r$ or θr, where θ is in radians. Perimeter of the sector is $s + 2r$. Once around a circle is $360°$ or 2π radians.

Trapezoid. $A = (h/2)(b_1 + b_2)$. $p = b_1 + n + b_2 + m$. b_1 is parallel to b_2. m is not parallel to n.

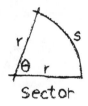

Cylinder. $V = \pi r^2 h$.

$$SA = \underset{\text{top}}{\pi r^2} + \underset{\text{bottom}}{\pi r^2} + \underset{\substack{\text{curved} \\ \text{surface}}}{2\pi rh} = 2\pi r(r + h)$$

Cone. $V = (1/3)\pi r^2 h$. When a 3-dimensional figure comes to a point, like a cone or pyramid, multiply volume of cylinder by 1/3.

Triangle. We will say lots about them. $A = \frac{1}{2}bh$. $p = a + b + c$.

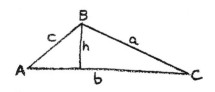

Isosceles triangle. Two sides equal (at least). BC base (unequal). AB, AC legs (equal). Angle A, vertex angle (unequal). Angles B and C, base angles (equal).

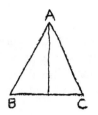

Equilateral triangle. All sides equal. All angles 60°, since the sum of the angles of a triangle is 180°. $p = 3s$. $h = s3^{1/2}/2$. $A = s^2 3^{1/2}/4$.

Right triangle. a,b legs (may be equal). c is hypotenuse (opposite right angle). You should know certain right triangles perfectly. Also $c^2 = a^2 + b^2$. 30°-60°-90°, sides s, $s3^{1/2}$, $2s$. Specifically if the hypotenuse is 2, opposite the 30° angle is 1, and opposite the 60° side is $3^{1/2}$. 45°-45°-90° sides s, s, $s2^{1/2}$. Specifically, if opposite 45° is 1, hypotenuse is $2^{1/2}$.

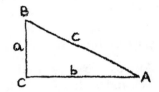

All of these are needed for trig plus the following groups: 3,4,5 (largest is always the hypotenuse), 6,8,10, 9,12,15, etc. (for this one, since it appears in physics, you might learn the angles—37° approx., 53° approx., 90° exact); 5,12,13 (10,24,26); 8,15,17; 7,24,25. There are others, but it pays to learn these because they come up over and over and over and over.

Other terms: (1) SUPPLEMENTARY—2 angles whose sum is 180°. (2) COMPLEMENTARY—2 angles whose sum is 90°. (Note the spelling—"complimentary" means "How attractive all you readers are," a compliment. Also note: I hate measures of angles, for those of you who know what that is.)

7. DISTANCE FORMULA, MIDPOINT, CIRCLES, AND PARABOLAS

Definition   DISTANCE — The distance between 2 points (x_1, y_1) and (x_2, y_2) is given by the formula $d = [(x_2 - x_1)^2 + (y_2 - y_1)^2]^{1/2}$.

Definition   MIDPOINT — The average (mean) between 2 points is $\left((x_1 + x_2)/2, (y_1 + y_2)/2\right)$.

EXAMPLE 1   Given $(3, -5)$ and $(9, -1)$. Find the length of the line segment between the points and the midpoint of that line segment.

$$d = [(9 - 3)^2 + (-1 - (-5)^2]^{1/2} = (36 + 16)^{1/2} = 52^{1/2}$$
$$= (2 \cdot 2 \cdot 13)^{1/2} = 2(13)^{1/2}$$

Midpoint is $\left((3 + 9)/2, (-1 + -5)/2\right) = (6, -3)$.

Definition   CIRCLE — Set of all points (x, y) at a distance r (don't tell anyone, but r stands for radius) from a given point (h, k) called the center of the circle.

The equation of a circle is the square of the distance formula $(x - h)^2 + (y - k)^2 = r^2$.

EXAMPLE 2   Find the center and radius of $(x - 3)^2 + (y + 5)^2 = 7$.
$C(3, -5)$ which is the opposite sign, and the radius $= 7^{1/2}$.

EXAMPLE 3   Find r and C for the circle $2x^2 + 2y^2 - 12x + 6y + 8 = 0$.

First, we know it's a circle since the coefficients of x^2 and y^2 are the same, as long as the radius turns out to be a positive number.

$$2x^2 + 2y^2 - 12x + 6y + 8 = 0 \quad \text{or} \quad x^2 + y^2 - 6x + 3y + 4 = 0$$

Co-efficients of x^2 and y^2 must be 1

$$\text{or} \quad x^2 - 6x + y^2 + 3y = -4$$

Group x's and y's together, constant to other side

$$\text{or} \quad x^2 - 6x + (-6/2)^2 + y^2 + 3y + (3/2)^2 = (-6/2)^2 + (3/2)^2 - 4$$

Complete the square and add the term(s) to each side

$$\text{or} \quad (x - 3)^2 + (y + 3/2)^2 = 29/4$$

Factor and do the arithmetic

The center is $(3, -3/2)$ and the radius is $29^{1/2}/2$.

Parabola

Later we will do a more complete study of the parabola. We need the basic, standard high school parabola for now. We will study parabolas of the form $y = ax^2 + bx + c$, $a \neq 0$. The coeff. of x^2 determines the parabola's shape.

 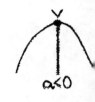

The low point (or high point), indicated by the letter V, is the vertex, which is why the letter V is usually used.

The x coordinate of the vertex is found by setting x equal to $-b/(2a)$. The y value is gotten by putting the x value into the equation for the parabola. The line through the vertex, the axis of symmetry, is given by $x = -b/(2a)$. The intercepts plus the vertex usually are enough for a fairly good picture. We will do some now.

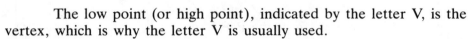

EXAMPLE 4 $y = 2x^2 - 7x + 3$

Vertex $x = -b/(2a) = -(-7)/2(2) = 7/4$

$y = 2(7/4)^2 - 7(7/4) + 3 = -25/8 \qquad (7/4, -25/8)$

Axis of symmetry $x = -b/(2a) \qquad x = 7/4$

y-intercept $x = 0$, $y = 3 \qquad (0,3)$

x-intercepts $y = 0$

$2x^2 - 7x + 3 = (2x - 1)(x - 3) = 0$

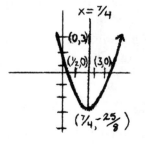

$x = \frac{1}{2}$, 3 and the intercepts are $(\frac{1}{2}, 0)$ and $(3,0)$. The graph opens upward.

EXAMPLE 5 $y = x^2 + 6x$

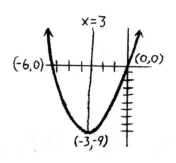

Vertex $x = -b/(2a) = -6/2(1) = -3$

$y = (-3)^2 + 6(-3) = -9$ $(-3, -9)$

x-intercepts $y = 0$

$x^2 + 6x = x(x + 6) = 0$

$x = 0, -6$—$(0, 0)$ also the y-intercept $(-6, 0)$. Picture is UP. Axis of sym $x = -3$.

EXAMPLE 6 $y = 9 - x^2$

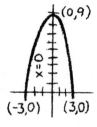

Vertex $x = -b/(2a) = 0/2(-1) = 0$

$y = 9$ $(0, -9)$ also y-intercept

x-intercepts $y = 0$

$0 = 9 - x^2 = (3 - x)(3 + x)$

$x = 3, -3$, intercepts are $(3, 0)$ and $(-3, 0)$. Picture is DOWN. Axis of sym $x = 0$.

EXAMPLE 7 $y = x^2 - 2x + 5$

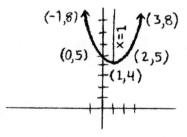

Vertex $x = -(-2)/2(1) = 1$

$y = 1^2 - 2(1) + 5$ $(1, 4)$

y-intercept $(0, 5)$. $y = x^2 - 2x + 5 = 0$. Quadratic formula gives imaginary roots, sooo no x-intercepts.

To get more points, make a chart. Take 2 or 3 x values (integers) just below the vertex and 2 or 3 just above.

x	y
−1	8
0	5
1	4
2	5
3	8

Axis of sym $x = 1$. Parabola is UP.

We are now ready for functions.

8. FUNCTIONS

One of the most neglected topics in high school is the study of functions. In this book there will be 3 rather lengthy chapters directly related to functions, and several others indirectly related. There are 2 reasons for this: functions are important, and most calculus courses assume you know this topic almost perfectly, an unrealistic assumption. So let's get started at the beginning.

FUNCTION: Given a set D. To each element in D, we assign 1 and only 1 element.

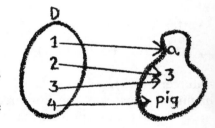

EXAMPLE 1   Does the picture here represent a function? The answer is yes. 1 goes into a, 2 goes into 3, 3 goes into 3, and 4 goes into a pig. Each element in D is assigned 1 and only 1 element.

The next example will show what is not a function. But let us talk a little more about this example. The set D is called the DOMAIN. We usually think about x values when we think about the domain. This is not necessarily true but is true in nearly all high school and college courses, so we will assume it.

There is a second set that arises. It is not part of the definition. However it is always there. It is called the RANGE. Notice the domain and the range can contain the same thing (the number 3) or vastly different things (3 and a pig). However, in math, we deal mostly with numbers and letters. The rule (the arrows) is called the MAP or MAPPING. 1 is mapped into a; 2 is mapped into 3; 3 is mapped into 3; and 4 is mapped into a pig.

Functional notation

The rule is usually given in a different form: f(1) = a (read "f of one equals a"); f(2) = 3; f(3) = 3; and f(4) = pig.

28

Note 1:   When we think of the range, we will think of the y values, although again this is not necessarily true.

Note 2:   We cannot always draw pictures of functions, and we will give more realistic examples after we give an example of something that is not a function.

EXAMPLE 2   The picture here does not represent a function, since 1 is assigned 2 values, a and d.

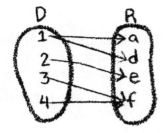

EXAMPLE 3   Let $f(x) = x^2 + 4x + 7$. $D = \{1, -3, 10\}$.

$f(1) = (1)^2 + 4(1) + 7 = 12$

$f(-3) = (-3)^2 + 4(-3) + 7 = 4$

$f(10) = (10)^2 + 4(10) + 7 = 147$

The range would be $\{4, 12, 147\}$. If we graphed these points, we would graph $(1, 12)$, $(-3, 4)$, and $(10, 147)$.

Note: Instead of graphing points (x, y), we are graphing points $(x, f(x))$. For our purposes, the notation is different, but the meanings are the same.

EXAMPLE 4   Let $g(x) = x^2 - 5x - 9$. $D = \{4, 0, -3, a^4, x + h\}$. Find the elements in the range.

This is a pretty crazy example, but there are reasons to do it.

$g(4) = (4)^2 - 5(4) - 9 = -13 \qquad g(0) = 0^2 - 5(0) - 9 = -9$

$g(-3) = (-3)^2 - 5(-3) - 9 = 15 \qquad g(a^4) = (a^4)^2 - 5a^4 - 9$

$\qquad = a^8 - 5a^4 - 9 \qquad g(x + h) = (x + h)^2 - 5(x + h) - 9$

$\qquad = x^2 + 2xh + h^2 - 5x - 5h - 9$

Wherever there is an x, you replace it by x + h!

The range is $\{-13, -9, 15, a^8 - 5a^4 - 9, x^2 + 2xh + h^2 - 5x - 5h - 9\}$.

EXAMPLE 5 $f(x) = x/(x + 5)$. Find $\dfrac{f(x + h) - f(x)}{h}$.

$$\frac{f(x+h)-f(x)}{h} = \frac{\dfrac{x+h}{x+h+5} - \dfrac{x}{x+5}}{h}$$

Add the fractions. Two tricks: $a/b - c/d =$ $(ad - bc)/bd$; $(e/f)/h = e/fh$

$$= \frac{(x+h)(x+5) - x(x+h+5)}{(x+h+5)(x+5)h}$$

Multiply out the top; never multiply out the bottom

$$= \frac{5h}{(x+h+5)(x+5)h} = \frac{5}{(x+h+5)(x+5)}$$

Cancel the h's

This kind of problem occurs in almost every precalc book. What you should ask is why the heck is it here? I will tell you. This is very close to the first topic you do in calculus. Here is a preview.

We have learned that the slope of a straight line is always the same. However if we draw any curve and draw all its tangent lines, the slope changes. We would like to study this and algebratize it.

Given the point P(x,f(x)). A little bit away from P is point Q. Its x value is x + h, where x + h is an x value a little bit away from x. (In order for you to see it, Q is a lot away from P.) If the first co-ordinate is x + h, the second co-ord. is f(x + h). Draw PQ, PR (horizontal line), and QR (vertical line). On any horizontal line all y values are the same. P and R have the same y values. Q and R have the same x values.

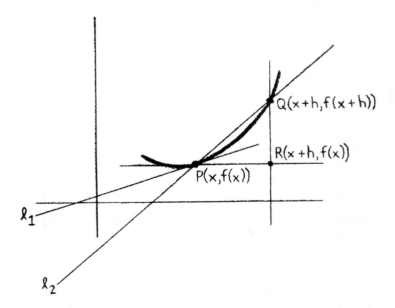

Since Q and R have the same x values, the length of QR, which is the change in y or Δy, is f(x + h) − f(x). Since P and R have the same y values, the length of PR, which is the change in x or Δx, is (x + h) − x = h.

The slope of the secant line ℓ_2 joining the points P and Q is

$$\frac{\Delta y}{\Delta x} = \frac{f(x + h) - f(x)}{h}$$

which is why we study this expression. But here's the conclusion. If we let h go to 0, graphically it means the point [x + h,f(x + h)] gets closer and closer to [x,f(x)]. If we do this process to the left of P as well as here to the right of P, and if they both approach the line ℓ_1, then what we have calculated is the slope of the tangent line ℓ_1 at the point [x,f(x)]!!!!! You have taken your first step into calculus!!!!!

1 − 1 function. 1 − 1 is a property we need occasionally.

Definition — If f(a) = f(b), then a = b.

EXAMPLES 6 and 7   f(x) = 2x is 1 − 1, but g(x) = x^2 is not 1 − 1.

If f(a) = f(b),   If g(a) = g(b),

then 2a = 2b   then $a^2 = b^2$.

and a = b.   But a could equal b or −b. Therefore not 1 − 1.

How to tell a function by sight. Use the vertical line test. If, for every vertical line, each line hits the curve once and only once, then we have a function (for each x value, there is only 1 y value). If there is 1 vertical line which hits a curve twice, the curve is not a function.

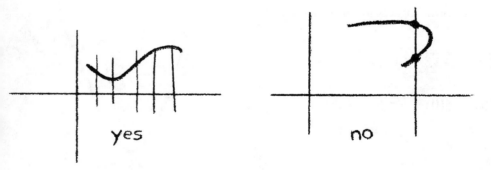

Finding the ranges and domains and sketches of functions (beginning).

EXAMPLE 8   f(x) = 3x + 1

This should look familiar. It looks like y = 3x + 1. If you graph it, you will find that it is. It is an oblique (slanted) straight line. Any such line has domain and range, all real numbers. Let's graph it.

x	f(x)	
−1	−2	(−1,−2)
0	1	(0,1)
2	7	(2,7)

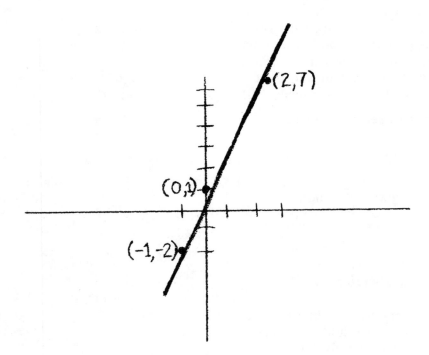

EXAMPLE 9 $f(x) = x^2 + 6x + 5$

This is, of course, the parabolic function we did before. Let's do it once more.

Vertex $x = -b/(2a) = -6/2(1) = -3$. $f(-3) = (-3)^2 + 6(-3) + 5 = -4$. $(-3,-4)$.

y-intercept $x = 0$. $f(0) = (0)^2 + 6(0) + 5 = 5$. $(0,5)$.

x-intercepts: $f(x) = 0 = x^2 + 6x + 5 = (x + 5)(x + 1)$.
   $x = -5, -1$. $(-5,0)$, $(-1,0)$.

Let's do some functions that are not repeats.

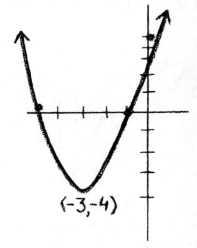

EXAMPLE 10 $f(x) = |3x + 5|$

In graphing an absolute value, we should note the shape is a V, or a Λ if there is a minus sign in front of the absolute value. We find the vertex first by setting $3x + 5 = 0$ or $x = -5/3$. We then make a chart, taking two x values (only integers to make life easier for us) less than $-5/3$ and two greater than $-5/3$. Then we graph.

x	$\lvert 3x + 5 \rvert$
−3	4
−2	1
−5/3	0
−1	2
0	5

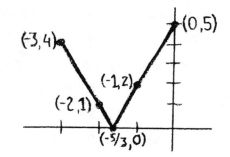

The domain is all real numbers. The range is all numbers greater than or equal to zero.

EXAMPLE 11 $g(x) = \sqrt{x + 2}$

Domain is $x + 2 \geq 0$ or $x \geq -2$. Range $y \geq 0$ (pos square root). The object is to pick values so that the square root is exact. The values $-2, -1, 2, 7$ will do the trick.

x	$\sqrt{x + 2}$
−2	0
−1	1
2	2
7	3

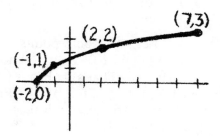

EXAMPLE 12 $F(x) = \sqrt{25 - x^2}$

The domain is $25 - x^2 = (5 - x)(5 + x) \geq 0$. If we do the inequalities as before, we get the domain $-5 \leq x \leq 5$. However we can use a trick. If we square both sides and get the x^2 on the left, we get $x^2 + y^2 = 25$, a circle center at the origin, radius 5. However since $y \geq 0$, it is only the top half of the circle.

From the graph here we see the range is $0 \leq y \leq 5$.

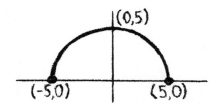

EXAMPLE 13 $f(x) = x / \lvert x \rvert$

This is an example that is needed for the future. For any value bigger than 0, no matter how close to 0, f(positive) = 1. Similarly f(negative) = −1. f(0) undefined. Domain is all x except 0. Range $\{1, -1\}$.

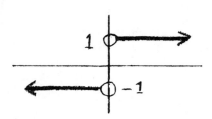

The open dot means exactly as before. $(0, -1)$ and $(0, 1)$ are not part of the answer, but everything up to that point is.

We next get to a group of functions that almost everyone has trouble with. Please study this example carefully. We also need 2 new related notations:

2^+—a number close (very close) to 2, bigger than 2, such as 2.00001.

2^-—a number very close to 2 but smaller than 2, such as 1.9999999.

We are now ready for this example, a function defined in pieces.

$$
\begin{aligned}
f(x) &= x^2 & x &< 0 & (1)\\
&= 6 & x &= 0 & (2)\\
&= x+2 & 0 &< x < 2 & (3)\\
&= 7 & x &= 2 & (4)\\
&= 6-x & 2 &< x \le 4 & (5)\\
&= 2 & x &> 4 & (6)
\end{aligned}
$$

There are 6 parts. (1) is half a parabola. (2) is the point (0,6). (3) is a line segment minus the 2 ends. (4) is the point (2,7). (5) is another line segment, minus the left end. (6) is a ray minus the left end.

Let's try some points. From (1), $f(-3) = 9$, $f(-2) = 4$, $f(-1) = 1$, and $f(0^-) = 0^+$—an open dot on the point (0,0). From (2), $f(0) = 6$. That's it. From (3), $f(0^+) = 0^+ + 2 = 2^+$, an open dot on (0,2). $f(1) = 3$. $f(2^-) = 4^-$. From (4), $f(2) = 7$. From (5), $f(2^+) = 6 - 2^+ = 4^-$ (6 minus a little more than 2 is a little less than 4)—an open dot on (2,4). $f(3) = 3$. $f(4) = 2$ (no need for 4^-). Finally from (6), $f(4^+) = 2$ [note (5) and (6) come together], $f(5) = 2$, $f(6) = 2$, forever $= 2$.

Let us put this in chart form and graph this function.

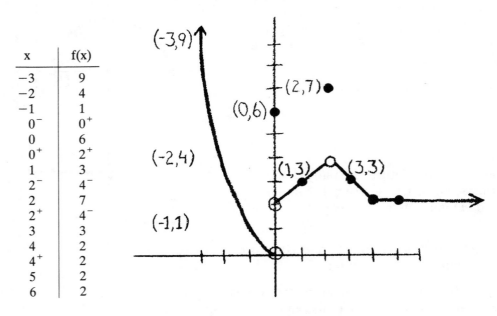

x	f(x)
-3	9
-2	4
-1	1
0^-	0^+
0	6
0^+	2^+
1	3
2^-	4^-
2	7
2^+	4^-
3	3
4	2
4^+	2
5	2
6	2

This is not easy, but it is important. This example should be gone over a good number of times.

9. COMPOSITE AND INVERSE FUNCTIONS

COMPOSITE FUNCTIONS

Suppose we have a function, map f, whose domain is D and range R_1. Suppose also we have another function, map g, domain R_1, and range R_2. Is there a map that goes from the original domain D to the last range R_2? The answer is of course yes; otherwise why would I waste your time writing this paragraph?

Definition   Given a function, map f, domain D, range R_1. Given a second function, map g, domain R_1, range R_2. Define the composite map $g \circ f$, domain D, range R_2. $(g \circ f)(x)$, read "g circle f of x," is $g[f(x)]$, read "g of f of x." The picture might look as shown here:

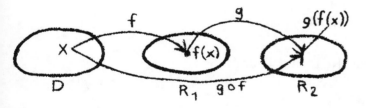

EXAMPLE 1   Suppose $f(x) = x^2 + 4$ and $g(x) = 2x + 5$.

1. $g(f(3))$. $f(3) = 3^2 + 4 = 13$. $g(13) = 2(13) + 5 = 31$. The picture is as shown here:

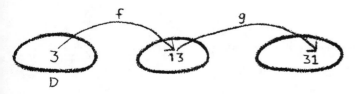

2. $f[g(3)]$. First, let's note that the picture would be totally different. Second, the "inside" map always is done first. $g(3) =$

$2(3) + 5 = 11$. $f(11) = 11^2 + 4 = 125$. Rarely are the 2 composites the same.

3. $g(f(x))$. $g(x) = 2x + 5$. This means multiply the point by 2 and add 5. $g(f(x))$ means the point is no longer x but f(x). The rule is multiply f(x) by 2 and add 5. So $g(f(x)) = 2(f(x)) + 5 = 2(x^2 + 4) + 5 = 2x^2 + 13$. **Note:** $g(f(3)) = 2(3)^2 + 13 = 31$, which agrees with item 1 above.

4. $f(g(x))$. $f(x) = x^2 + 4$. So $f(g(x)) = (g(x))^2 + 4 = (2x + 5)^2 + 4 = 4x^2 + 20x + 29$. $f(g(3)) = 4(3)^2 + 20(3) + 29 = 125$, which agrees with item 2, as it must.

INVERSE FUNCTIONS

There is a function which takes the domain into the range. Is there a function which takes the range back into the domain? The answer is yes under certain circumstances. That circumstance is when the domain and range are in $1 - 1$ correspondence. This means every element in the domain can be paired off with 1 and only 1 element in the range. In the case of a finite set, $1 - 1$ correspondence means the same number of elements.

On a graph you can see if you have an inverse by first using the vertical line test (each line hits the graph only once) to see if the curve is a function. Then use the horizontal line test (each line hits the curve, also, only once) to determine if there is an inverse function. The most common kinds of functions that have inverses are ones that always increase or always decrease.

The definition of an inverse function is very long, but it is not very difficult, after you read the definition and the examples that follow:

Given a function, map f, domain D, range R, D and R are in $1 - 1$ correspondence. Define f^{-1}, read "f inverse," domain R, range D. If originally a was an element of D and b was an element of R, define $f^{-1}(b) = a$ if originally $f(a) = b$.

This looks quite bad, but really it is not. Look at the picture here.

Ex. 1

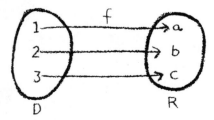
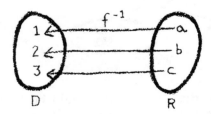

$f^{-1}(a) = 1$ because originally $f(1) = a$; $f^{-1}(b) = 2$ since $f(2) = b$; and $f^{-1}(c) = 3$ 'cause $f(3) = c$.

A little better? Let's make it much better. First note the inverses we know: adding and subtracting, multiplying and dividing (except with zero), squaring and square roots, providing only 1 square root, cubing and cube roots, etc.

EXAMPLE 2 Given map $f(x) = 2x + 3$, domain $\{1,8,30\}$.

$f(1) = 5$, $f(8) = 19$, $f(30) = 63$. The range is $\{5,19,63\}$. D and R are in 1–1 corresp. Let's find the inverse. The domain and range switch. The new domain is $\{5,19,63\}$. Let us find the new map, f^{-1}. $f(x) = 2x + 3$ means multiply by 2 and add 3. Going in the opposite direction, add 3 was last, so subtract 3 is first. First we multiply by 2; going backward the last thing is divide by 2.

$f(x) = 2x + 3$. $2x + 3 = f(x)$. $2x = f(x) - 3$. $x = [f(x) - 3]/2$. Notation change: $f(x)$ is now in the new domain. Change $f(x)$ to x! x is the new function; so x becomes $f^{-1}(x)$. So our new function is $f^{-1}(x) = (x - 3)/2$, $D = \{5,19,63\}$. Let's check it out!! $f^{-1}(5) = (5 - 3)/2 = 1$. OK so far. $f^{-1}(19) = (19 - 3)/2 = 8$. $f^{-1}(63) = (63 - 3)/2 = 30$. Everything is OK.

Let's do some more examples.

EXAMPLE 3

$$f(x) = \frac{x + 2}{x - 3}$$

The domain is all reals except x = 3 since bottom of a fraction may never be equal to 0. However it is not clear at all what the range is. Let's find the inverse function. Perhaps the original range and the new domain will become more obvious. In order to make this less messy, let f(x) = y

$$\frac{y}{1} = \frac{x + 2}{x - 3}$$

Multiply through by x − 3

$$y(x - 3) = x + 2$$
$$yx - 3y = x + 2$$
$$yx - x = 3y + 2$$
$$x(y - 1) = 3y + 2$$

$$x = \frac{3y + 2}{y - 1}$$

At this point it is clear the old range was all y values except for 1. Now notation change

$$f^{-1}(x) = \frac{3x + 2}{x - 1}$$

Note: Sometimes, in order to find the range, it is a good idea to solve for x!!!!

EXAMPLE 4   Find the inverse map for $f(x) = \sqrt{3x + 1}$ with the domain $x \geq 1$ and the range $y \geq 2$.
Let $f(x) = y$. $y = \sqrt{3x + 1}$.

$$\sqrt{3x + 1} = y$$
$$3x + 1 = y^2$$
$$3x = y^2 - 1$$
$$x = (y^2 - 1)/3$$
so $f^{-1}(x) = (x^2 - 1)/3$, $x \geq 2$

As we go along in the book, we will have more inverses. That's it for now.

10. TRIGONOMETRY

I have always thought that trigonometry should be the easiest of all math courses. It requires very little of the past: some elementary algebra, like factoring, multiplying terms, adding fractions, and solving simple equations; a little intermediate algebra; and a small amount of geometry. It does require a fair amount of memorization. I will try to convince you how easy the course should be.

ANGLES

There are 3 basic measures of angles: revolutions, degrees, and radians. The one we know the best is degrees. A DEGREE is 1/360th of a circle. It is a purely artificial measurement, probably found only on the planet Earth in the entire universe, where hopefully there is a lot more intelligent life.

A REVOLUTION is once around a circle. We actually use this measurement, although you may not recognize it. The speed of a car engine or a record is measured in RPMs, or revolutions per minute. A 45-RPM record is 45 revolutions per minute.

The most important measurement, used in calculus because it is a pure number, is radian. A RADIAN, approximately 57°, is gotten by putting the length of the radius on the circumference. The central angle formed by the 2 radii is a radian. There are 2π radians in a circle.

Here is a convenient chart which shows you how to change from 1 measurement to the other. It is a "multiply by" chart. Multiply the left column by the factor in the chart to give the top of the second, third, or fourth column.

to→ from↓	rev	deg	rad
rev	1	360	2π
deg	$\frac{1}{360}$	1	$\frac{\pi}{180}$
rad	$\frac{1}{2\pi}$	$\frac{180}{\pi}$	1

EXAMPLE 1 Change 7.5 revolutions to degrees and radians.
$7.5(2\pi) = 15\pi$ radians. $7.5(360°) = 2700°$.

EXAMPLE 2 Change 30° to radians. $30(\pi/180) = \pi/6$.

EXAMPLE 3 Change $\pi/4$ to degrees. $(\pi/4)(180/\pi) = 45°$.

You must be able to do examples 2 and 3 very quickly. It would also be extremely beneficial if you knew the following angles: $30° = \pi/6$; $45° = \pi/4$; $60° = \pi/3$; $90° = \pi/2$; $180° = \pi$; $270° = 3\pi/2$; $360° = 2\pi$. The more multiples of 30°,45°, and 60° you know, the easier things will be. Remember I am trying to make things as easy as possible, but there is much memorization on your part.

Note: Many books break down degrees. There are 60 minutes to a degree, and 60 seconds to a minute. Modern treatment uses tenths and hundredths of degrees. Using minutes and seconds to me is both too old-fashioned and, even worse, too picky. Therefore, I round off all angles to the NEAREST DEGREE.

BASIC DEFINITIONS

On this planet angles are measured positively in a counterclockwise direction as indicated by the picture here. We locate the point (x,y), label r, where $r = (x^2 + y^2)^{1/2}$, the distance to the origin, and is, therefore, always positive. Define the following:

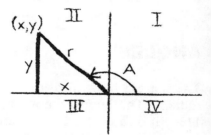

Sine of A = sin A = y/r   Cosine of A = cos A = x/r

Tangent of A = tan A = y/x   Cotangent of A = cot A = x/y

Secant of A = sec A = r/x   Cosecant of A = csc A = r/y

Note 1: When you get the point (x,y), the triangle formed must always be to the x-axis, either down or up to it.

Note 2: You must know these definitions PERFECTLY!!!!!

Note 3: The quadrant will tell you the sign of the trig function:

In quadrant I, x and y are positive (as r always is)—all trig functions are positive.

In II, x is negative—only sine and cosecant are positive.

In III, x and y are negative—only tangent and cotangent are positive.

In IV, y is negative—cosine and secant are positive.

Note 4: You must also know Note 3 perfectly.

MULTIPLES OF 30°,45°,60°,90°

You must be able to find all multiples of the above angles WITHOUT a calculator. First the 3 basics. Note that you do NOT have to memorize these. You should NOT memorize these. If you can draw the triangles and know the definitions, that will be enough.

Ex 1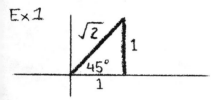

Ex 2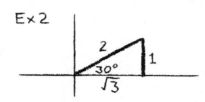

Ex 3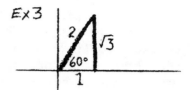

$\sin 45° = y/r = 1/2^{1/2}$

$\cos 45° = x/r = 1/2^{1/2}$

$\tan 45° = y/x = 1/1 = 1$

$\cot 45° = x/y = 1/1 = 1$

$\sec 45° = r/x = 2^{1/2}/1 = 2^{1/2}$

$\csc \pi/4 = r/y = 2^{1/2}/1 = 2^{1/2}$

$\sin 30° = 1/2$

$\cos 30° = 3^{1/2}/2$

$\tan 30° = 1/3^{1/2}$

$\cot 30° = 3^{1/2}/1 = 3^{1/2}$

$\sec 30° = 2/3^{1/2}$

$\csc \pi/6 = 2/1 = 2$

$\sin 60° = 3^{1/2}/2$

$\cos 60° = 1/2$

$\tan 60° = 3^{1/2}/1 = 3^{1/2}$

$\cot 60° = 1/3^{1/2}$

$\sec 60° = 2/1 = 2$

$\csc \pi/3 = 2/3^{1/2}$

Note 1: When you draw the triangles really make them look correct (also use the ruler). In 45°-45°-90° triangles, make x and y equal. In the 30°-60°-90° triangles, make the short side (opposite the 30°) shorter than the longer leg (opposite the 60°).

Note 2: Your teacher might have you rationalize some of these, such as $1/2^{1/2} = 2^{1/2}/2$, by multiplying top and bottom by the square root of 2.

EXAMPLE 4 Find cos 240°.

$240° = 90° + 90° + 60°$; 60° angle in the third quadrant. $3^{1/2}$ opposite the 60° angle, 1 opposite the 30°, and both negative (negative to the left, negative down); $r = 2$ and positive since r is always positive. $\cos 240° = \cos 4\pi/3 = x/r = -1/2$.

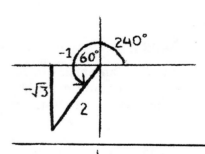

EXAMPLE 5 Find sin 135°.

$135° = 90° + 45° = 180° - 45°$. $1 - 1 - \sqrt{2}$ triangle. x neg, to the left; y pos, up; $r = 2^{1/2}$ always pos. $\sin 135° = \sin 3\pi/4 = y/r = 1/2^{1/2}$.

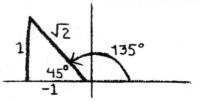

EXAMPLE 6 Find tan 330°.

$300° = 90° + 90° + 90° + 60° = 360° - 30°$. $x = 3^{1/2}$ and is positive (to the right). $y = -1$ and is negative (down). $r = 2$ and is always positive. $\tan 330° = \tan 11\pi/6 = y/x = -1/3^{1/2}$.

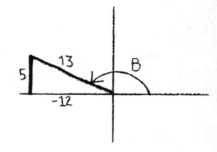

Note: If θ is an angle in the first quadrant, the *related angles* are $180° - \theta$ in the second quadrant, $180° + \theta$ in the third quadrant, and $360° - \theta$ in the fourth quadrant. The related angles all have the same picture. The value of the trig function is the same except for the sign. $\cos 60° = \frac{1}{2}$. $\cos 120° = \cos(180° - 60°) = -\frac{1}{2}$. $\cos 240° = \cos(180° + 60°) = -\frac{1}{2}$. $\cos 300° = \cos(360° - 60°) = \frac{1}{2}$. These should not be memorized. You can and should draw these pictures, first to see that these are the same triangle, and then to practice drawing until you become very, very good.

EXAMPLE 7 Suppose cot A is $-7/6$ in IV. Write all the other trig functions of A. (This example should have preceded 30°-60°-90° section.)

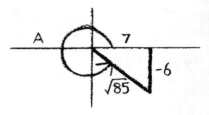

In IV, x pos, y neg, r pos. $\cot A = x/y$. Let $x = 7$, $y = -6$, $r = [7^2 + (-6)^2]^{1/2} = 85^{1/2}$. $\sin A = y/r = -6/85^{1/2}$. $\cos A = x/r = 7/85^{1/2}$. $\tan A = y/x = -6/7$. $\cot A = x/y = -7/6$. $\sec A = r/x = 85^{1/2}/7$. $\csc A = r/y = 85^{1/2}/(-6)$.

EXAMPLE 8 $\sin B = 5/13$ in II. Find sec B.

Let $y = 5$ and $r = 13$. $x^2 + 5^2 = 13^2$. $x = \pm(144)^{1/2} = \pm 12$. -12 since x is negative in II. $\sec B = r/x = 13/-12$.

Note: If you memorized Pythagorean triples, you would know this is 5-12-13. **Also note:** This should have also preceded the 30°-60°-90° section. Now we are in the correct spot.

EXAMPLE 9 Find all the trig functions of 270°.

If you draw an angle of 270° or any multiple of 90°, it will fall on an axis—in this case on the negative y-axis. We let $r = 1$ in this case. So the point will be $(0, -1)$, $x = 0$ and $y = -1$. Now we can get all the trig functions.

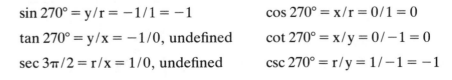

$\sin 270° = y/r = -1/1 = -1$ $\cos 270° = x/r = 0/1 = 0$

$\tan 270° = y/x = -1/0$, undefined $\cot 270° = x/y = 0/-1 = 0$

$\sec 3\pi/2 = r/x = 1/0$, undefined $\csc 270° = r/y = 1/-1 = -1$

Note: For all multiples of 90°, 2 trig functions will always be 0, 2 will always be undefined, and 2 will either both be -1 or both be $+1$.

CURVE SKETCHING

We will sketch basic sine, cosine, and tangent functions. The techniques for sketching the secant and cosecant are the same as the sine and cosine except for a different picture, and the cotangent is likewise similar to the tangent. All of the trig functions are PERIODIC. That is, after a while, they repeat. The technical definition of "periodic" is $f(x + p) = f(x)$ for all x. If p is the smallest positive such number, p is called the PERIOD. The period of the sine, cosine, secant, and cosecant is 360° or 2π. The period of tangent and the cotangent is 180° or π. If we graph $y = \sin x$ by taking 0,30,45,60,90,120,135,150,180,210,225,240,270,300,315,330, and 360 degrees, the picture would look as shown here.

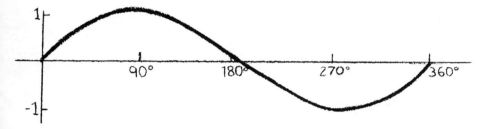

Doing the same for $y = \cos x$, we get the second picture here.

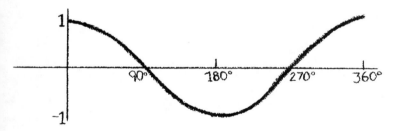

Doing the same for $y = \tan x$, except only up to 180°, we get the third picture.

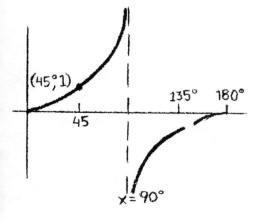

There is an asymptote (a line the curve gets very close to at the end but does not hit), which we will discuss later. On the tangent curve, we label 1 point, the $\frac{1}{4}$ point. $\tan 45° = 1$.

Note 1: In sketching a curve, you will be normally asked to graph 5 points: beginning, end, 1/4, 1/2, 3/4 points.

Note 2: A sneaky (but good) way of calculating, say, sin x at multiples of 90° is to look at the intercepts (0°,180°,360°), high point, and 270°, the low point. Try it. You'll like it.

There are 4 things we consider in the sketching: amplitude, period, shift up and down, and the phase (left and right shift). The technical definition of the AMPLITUDE is the maximum value minus the minimum value divided by 2. Tangent, cotangent, secant, cosecant have no amplitude since their maxes are plus infinity and their mins are minus infinity. For $y = A \sin x$ or $y = A \cos x$, the amplitude is the absolute value of A.

We will work in degrees because it is easier.

EXAMPLE 10 $y = 10 \sin x$. The sketch is the same as $y = \sin x$ except the high point is 10 and the low point is -10.

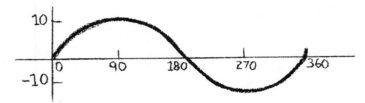

EXAMPLE 11 $y = -4 \cos x$. Amplitude is 4. Curve is upside down!

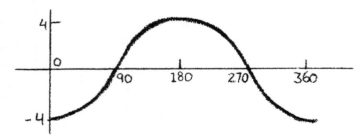

Easy so far? It really shouldn't get much harder.

EXAMPLE 12 $y = \sin 5x$. The amplitude is 1. The period is $360°/5 = 72°$.

For sin x the 5 points are 0,90,180,270,360°. Now divide them by 5. The 5 points are 0,18,36,54, and 72 degrees. The curve is the sine curve.

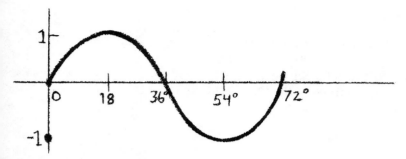

EXAMPLE 13 $y = -7\cos 2x$. Amplitude 7. Upside down, period $360°/2 = 180°$.

0,90,180,270,360 divided by 2 are 0,45,90,135,180. Cosine curve.

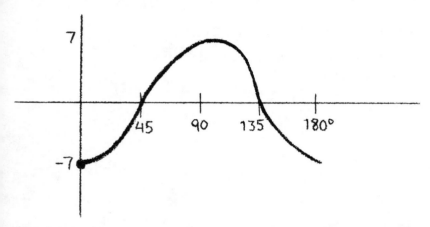

EXAMPLE 14 $y = 4\tan 3x$. No amplitude. Right-side-up. Period $180°/3 = 60°$.

Points 0,45,90,135,180 divided by 3 become 0,15,30,45,60. Asymptote at the middle or 30°. The $\frac{1}{4}$ point 15° is (15°,4). This indicates the coefficient in front. Let us show: $y = 4\tan 3x = 4\tan 3(15°) = 4\tan 45° = 4(1) = 4$. (15°,4).

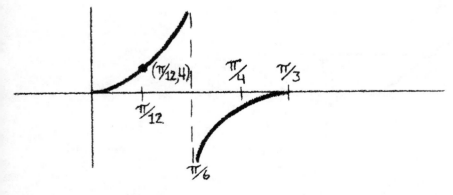

Note: If $y = \sin Bx$ or $\cos Bx$, period is $360°/|B|$. $\tan Bx$? Period is $180°/|B|$.

EXAMPLE 15 $y = 5 \sin (3x + 120)$. Factor the 3.

$y = 5 \sin 3(x + 40)$. Amplitude is 5. Right-side-up. Period $360°/3 =$ 120. 0,90,180,270,360 divided by 3 become 0,30,60,90,120. +40 is the left or right shift. +40 means a shift of 40° to the left. So we have to *subtract* 40° from each angle. $0 - 40, 30 - 40, 60 - 40, 90 - 40, 120 - 40$ or $-40, -10, 20, 50, 80$. Let me show you why. For $x = 0 - 40$, $5 \sin (3x + 120) = 5 \sin [3(-40) + 120] = 5 \sin 0 = 0$.

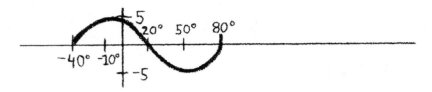

EXAMPLE 16 $y = 12 \cos (10x - 20)$. Amplitude 12. $y = 12 \cos 10(x - 2)$.

Period $360°/10 = 36°$. Five points are 0,9,18,27,36. Phase shift is 2 to the *right*. $0 + 2, 9 + 2, 18 + 2, 27 + 2, 36 + 2$, or 2,11,20,29,38.

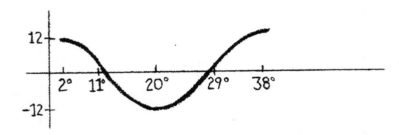

EXAMPLE 17 $y = \sin (\frac{1}{2}x + 50)$. Factor out $\frac{1}{2}$. $y = \sin \frac{1}{2}(x + 100)$.

Amplitude is 1. Period is $360°/\frac{1}{2} = 720°$. Shift 100 to the left. 0,90,180,270,360 become 0,180,360,540,720. Subtract 100; we get $-100,80,260,440,620$.

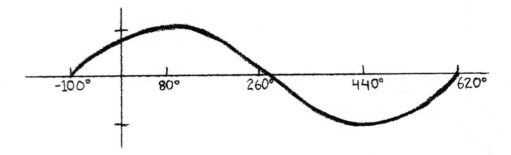

EXAMPLE 18 $3y - 12 = 6 \sin (3x - 60)$

$$3y = 6 \sin 3(x - 20) + 12$$

$$y = 2 \sin 3(x - 20) + 4$$

Note 3 in front of angle is unchanged

Amplitude is 2. Right-side-up. Period is 360°/3 = 120°. Shift 20 to the right. 0,90,180,270,360 become 0,30,60,90,120 become 20,50,80,110,140. Four on the right is a shift of the whole graph *up 4* (add 4 to each y value).

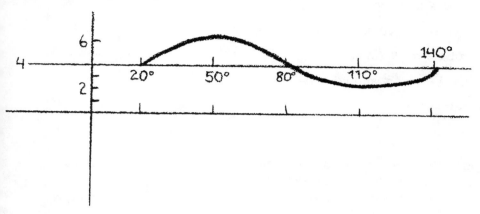

Note: Of course negative sign at the right (−4 instead of +4) would be a shift down.

If this does not look too hard, it shouldn't be. This should not take too much practice either.

IDENTITIES

This part of trig is important. It is also difficult for several reasons. Number 1 is that almost no book really teaches you how to attack identities. Number 2, no one method really works for all identities. Number 3, some of them require some thinking! Number 4 is that identities are 1 of the 4 or 5 areas of math that require a *lot* of practice!!!!!

First, we would like to know what an identity is.

Definition IDENTITY — An equation that is true for every value it is defined for.

EXAMPLE 19 $2x + 3x = 5x$. No matter what x you substitute, $2x + 3x = 5x$.

EXAMPLE 20 $4/x + 5/x = 9/x$. It is not defined for $x = 0$. Otherwise it is true.

The following are the most important trig identities (which are proven in virtually every book). In order to do this section you must know them perfectly in all forms. Here is the list:

1. $\sin x \csc x = 1$. $\sin x = 1/\csc x$ and $\csc x = 1/\sin x$.

2. $\cos x \sec x = 1$. $\cos x = 1/\sec x$ and $\sec x = 1/\cos x$.

3. $\tan x \cot x = 1$. $\tan x = 1/\cot x$ and $\cot x = 1/\tan x$.

4, 5. $\tan x = \sin x/\cos x$ and $\cot x = \cos x/\sin x$.

6. $\sin^2 x + \cos^2 x = 1$. $\sin^2 x = 1 - \cos^2 x$ and $\cos^2 x = 1 - \sin^2 x$.

7. $1 + \tan^2 x = \sec^2 x$. $\tan^2 x = \sec^2 x - 1$.

8. $1 + \cot^2 x = \csc^2 x$. $\cot^2 x = \csc^2 x - 1$.

You *must* know these perfectly. Say I came to your house in the middle of the night and said, "What is $\tan^2 x$ equal to?" You would mumble, "It is either $\sec^2 x - 1$ or $\sin^2 x/\cos^2 x$ or $1/\cot^2 x$. Now let me go back to sleep!!!!" When you do the identities, if you have not learned them yet, keep this list in front of you. It is VERY important to learn them. Am I repeating myself??!!

Following is a list of steps you should try, in the general order you should try them. Unlike solving first-degree equations, where if you follow the steps in precisely the right (and same) order, you will always get the correct answer, sometimes you must go back and sometimes you must skip steps. Sometimes even if you do a correct step, it might not be correct for this particular problem. But many times here you learn more from a wrong step than a right, as long as you remember for another problem. But you must keep trying. Only in that way will you get better.

Attacking identities

1. It is usually better to work with the more complicated side.

    A. Adding trig functions is more complicated than multiplication.

    B. Later on, double and half angles are more complicated than single angles—$\sin 2x$ or $\cos \frac{1}{2}x$ is more complicated than $\tan x$.

    C. In most books—the left side is the more complicated.

2. Do something "obvious." (I hate that word!)

    A. Add fractions.

    B. Multiply out a parenthesis.

    C. Square a term (a binomial).

3. If there is more than 1 term on the top and 1 term on the

bottom, split the fraction. In symbols $(a + b + c)/d =$ $\dfrac{a}{d} + \dfrac{b}{d} + \dfrac{c}{d}$.

4. If there is a known identity, use it.

5. If one side has only one trig function, try to write the other side in terms of that one.

6. Factor.

7. The "prayer" method. Multiply top and bottom by the same term and pray that everything works out.

8. If nothing else works, change everything to sines and cosines.

Note: Some people do step 8 first. It does work many times. However many times it makes the problem much longer since it always increases the number of terms.

Also note: Please do not get discouraged. For almost everybody, these manipulative skills do not come easily. Only through lots of practice and much heartache does anyone become good.

Now let us give some samples. Remember—patience and practice.

EXAMPLE 21

$$\frac{\tan x}{1 + \sec x} - \frac{\tan x}{1 - \sec x} = 2 \csc x \qquad \textbf{Add the fractions}$$

$$\frac{(\tan x)(1 - \sec x) - (\tan x)(1 + \sec x)}{(1 + \sec x)(1 - \sec x)} = \qquad \textbf{Multiply out top and bottom}$$

$$\frac{\tan x - (\tan x)(\sec x) - \tan x - (\tan x)(\sec x)}{1 - \sec^2 x} = \qquad \textbf{Simplify top; identity bottom}$$

$$\frac{-2(\tan x)(\sec x)}{-\tan^2 x} = \qquad \textbf{Reduce; change to sines and cosines and finally reduce. Then note the last identity}$$

$$\frac{2 \sec x}{\tan x} = \frac{2/\cos x}{\sin x / \cos x} = \frac{2}{\sin x} = 2 \csc x$$

Whew! Fortunately they are not all like this.

EXAMPLE 22

$$\frac{\cos x + \sin x - \sin^3 x}{\sin x} = \cot x + \cos^2 x \qquad \textbf{Split into 3 fractions}$$

$$\frac{\cos x}{\sin x} + \frac{\sin x}{\sin x} - \frac{\sin^3 x}{\sin x} = \qquad \textbf{Identity and algebra}$$

$$\cot x + 1 - \sin^2 x = \cot x + \cos^2 x \qquad \textbf{Identity}$$

EXAMPLE 23 $\sin^4 x - \cos^4 x = \sin^2 x - \cos^2 x$ **Factor the left—more complicated**

$(\sin^2 x - \cos^2 x)(\sin^2 x + \cos^2 x) = \sin^2 x - \cos^2 x$ $\sin^2 x + \cos^2 x = 1$

EXAMPLE 24 $\cos^4 x - 2\cos^2 x + 1 = \sin^4 x$ $\cos^2 x = 1 - \sin^2 x$

$(1 - \sin^2 x)^2 - 2(1 - \sin^2 x) + 1 =$

$1 - 2\sin^2 x + \sin^4 x - 2 + 2\sin^2 x + 1 = \sin^4 x$ **Hammer it out, simplifying**

EXAMPLE 25 $\dfrac{\sin x}{1 + \cos x} = \dfrac{1 - \cos x}{\sin x}$ **Prayer method—mult. top and bottom by $1 - \cos x$ and pray it works**

$\dfrac{(\sin x)(1 - \cos x)}{(1 + \cos x)(1 - \cos x)} =$ **Hint: Do not mult. out top because you want $1 - \cos x$ left on the top**

$\dfrac{(\sin x)(1 - \cos x)}{1 - \cos^2 x} =$ **Identity**

$\dfrac{(\sin x)(1 - \cos x)}{\sin^2 x} = \dfrac{1 - \cos x}{\sin x}$

   Well that's a sampling. Some are easy (when you see it); some are hard; some are long; some are short. Try to have fun. Learn from your wrong turns. But don't quit. Practice, and you will get better and better!!!!!

TRIG EQUATIONS

Trig equations are solved the same way as algebraic equations, with 2 differences: sometimes you use trig identities; and after you solve the equations, you still must solve for the angles.

   Trig equations seem a lot harder than they should be because most books group all of them together instead of talking about each individual kind. What I've tried to do is to give you 1 of most of the types.

EXAMPLE 26 $2\sin x - 3^{1/2} = 0$ **Let us start out slowly**

$\sin x = 3^{1/2}/2$ **Sine is positive in I and II. Draw the triangles!!!!!**

x = 60°

$\dfrac{\pi}{3}$

x = 120°

$\dfrac{2\pi}{3}$

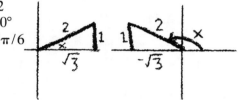

EXAMPLE 27

$2 \sin x \cos x - \cos x = 0$ **Take out a common factor**

$(\cos x)(2 \sin x - 1) = 0$

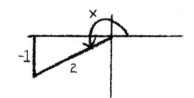

$\cos x = 0$
x = 90°, 270°
$\pi/2, 3\pi/2$

$\sin x = 1/2$
x = 30°, 150°
$\pi/6, 5\pi/6$

Note: When the sine or cosine $= 0$, $+1$, or -1, the angle is a multiple of 90°. The easiest way to find out which one is to draw $y = \sin x$ or $y = \cos x$ and look for the high points, low points, or intercepts.

EXAMPLE 28

$2 \sin^2 x - \sin x - 1 = 0$ **Factor the trinomial**

$(2 \sin x + 1)(\sin x - 1) = 0$ $\sin x = -\frac{1}{2}$ or $\sin x = 1$

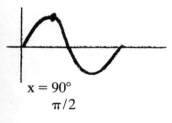

x = 90°

$\pi/2$

x = 210°, 330°

$7\pi/6, 11\pi/6$

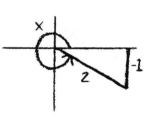

EXAMPLE 29 $3 \sin^2 x - 5 \sin x + 2 = 0$. $(3 \sin x - 2)(\sin x - 1) = 0$.
$\sin x = 1$; $\sin x = 2/3$ I,II.

As above, $\sin x = 1$ means x = 90° or $\pi/2$. $\sin x = 2/3$, in the first 2 quadrants, can only be found by using the calculator. Most calculators work this way to calculate the answer: 2 divided by 3 = inv, 2nd, sin. Answers are 42° and 180° − 42° = 138°.

EXAMPLE 30 $2 \sin^3 x - \sin x = 0$

A lot of answers. $(\sin x)(2 \sin^2 x - 1) = 0$. $\sin x = 0$ or $\sin^2 x = 1/2$. So $\sin x = \pm 1/2^{1/2}$.

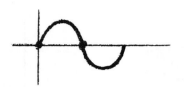 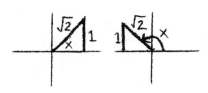 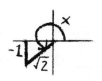 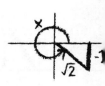

EXAMPLE 31 $\cos^2 x + \cos x - 1 = 0$. We must use the quadratic formula: $a = 1$, $b = 1$, $c = -1$.

$$\cos x = \frac{-b \pm (b^2 - 4ac)^{1/2}}{2a} = \frac{-1 \pm [1 - 4(1)(-1)]^{1/2}}{2(1)}$$

$$= \frac{-1 \pm 5^{1/2}}{2} = \frac{-1 \pm 2.24}{2}$$

One value is $(-1 - 2.24)/2 = -1.62$. No solution since the cosine is never less than -1. Another value is $(-1 + 2.24)/2 = .62$. Cosine positive in the first and fourth quadrant. Using the calculator we find $x = 52°$ and $360° - 52° = 308°$.

EXAMPLE 32 $\sin^2 x + \cos x - 1 = 0$. Trig substitution $\sin^2 x = 1 - \cos^2 x$.

$$(1 - \cos^2 x) + \cos x - 1 = 0 \qquad \text{or} \qquad -\cos^2 x + \cos x = 0$$

$$-\cos x(\cos x - 1) = 0 \qquad \cos x = 0 \text{ or } 1$$

$x = 0, 90°, 270°, 360°$ or 0, $\pi/2$, $3\pi/2$

EXAMPLE 33 $\tan^2 x + \sec x - 1 = 0$. Trig substitution $\tan^2 x = \sec^2 x - 1$.

$$(\sec^2 x - 1) + \sec x - 1 = 0 \qquad \text{or} \qquad \sec^2 x + \sec x - 2 = 0$$

$$(\sec x + 2)(\sec x - 1) = 0$$

$$\sec x = -2 \quad \text{or} \quad \cos x = -\tfrac{1}{2} \qquad\qquad \sec x = 1 \quad \text{or} \quad \cos x = 1$$

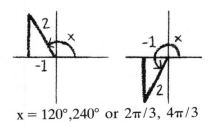 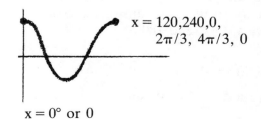

$x = 120, 240, 0,$
$\quad 2\pi/3, 4\pi/3, 0$

$x = 120°, 240°$ or $2\pi/3$, $4\pi/3$ $\qquad\qquad x = 0°$ or 0

EXAMPLE 34 $\sin x + \csc x = 2$. $\sin x + 1/\sin x = 2$ or $\sin^2 x + 1 = 2 \sin x$ or $\sin^2 x - 2 \sin x + 1 = 0$ or $(\sin x - 1)^2 = 0$ or $\sin x = 1$. So $x = 90°$ or $\pi/2$.

Let us wind up with a slightly messy one.

EXAMPLE 35 $\sin x - 3^{1/2} \cos x = 1$ **Isolate one of the trig functions, the messier one, the one with the square root of 3, and square both sides**

$\sin x - 1 = 3^{1/2} \cos x$

$(\sin x - 1)^2 = (3^{1/2} \cos x)^2$

$\sin^2 x - 2 \sin x + 1 = 3 \cos^2 x$ or $\sin^2 x - 2 \sin x + 1 = 3(1 - \sin^2 x)$

or $4 \sin^2 x - 2 \sin x - 2 = 0$ or $2(2 \sin x + 1)(\sin x - 1) = 0$

$\sin x = 1$ or $-\frac{1}{2}$. $x = 90°$ or $210°$ or $330°$.

Since we squared both sides, we may have introduced extraneous solutions or non-solutions. (This may also be the case if we start with a trig function in the denominator.) We must substitute the answers into the original equation.

$x = 90°$. $\sin 90° - 3^{1/2} \cos 90° = 1$. $1 - 0 = 1$. $90°$ is OK.

$x = 210°$. $\sin 210° - 3^{1/2} \cos 210° = 1$. $-\frac{1}{2} - 3^{1/2}(-3^{1/2}/2) = 1$.
    $-\frac{1}{2} + 3/2 = 1$. $210°$ is OK.

$x = 330°$. $\sin 330° - 3^{1/2} \cos 330° = 1$. $-\frac{1}{2} - 3^{1/2}(+3^{1/2}/2) = 1$.
    $-\frac{1}{2} - 3/2 \neq 1$. $330°$ is extraneous.

The answers are $90°$ and $210°$ or $\pi/2$ and $7\pi/6$.

DOMAINS AND RANGES OF THE TRIG FUNCTIONS

Let us list the ranges and domains of the trig functions. Then we will discuss.

	Domain	**Range**
$y = \sin x$	All reals	$-1 \leq y \leq 1$
$y = \cos x$	All reals	$-1 \leq y \leq 1$
$y = \tan x$	All reals except $90° \pm n180°$, n integer	All reals

y = cot x	All reals except $0° \pm n180°$	All reals
y = sec x	Same as tan x	All reals except $-1 < y < 1$
y = csc x	Same as cot x	Same as sec x

From the curve sketch, the domain and range for the sin x and cos x should be seen. tan x = y/x and sec x = r/x are defined everywhere except where the bottom, x, is 0. That occurs on the y-axis. The angles are 90°,270°,−90°, etc.

A similar argument for the domain of the cot x and csc x except the x-axis is no good. Angles are 0°,180°,−180°, etc. Range for the tangent is seen from the graph. The cotangent, the reciprocal of the tangent, is the same. The range for the sec x and csc x is the reciprocals of the sin x and cos x. However all can be +1 or −1.

It is of value to know this chart, especially sin x, cos x, and tan x.

DOUBLE ANGLES, HALF ANGLES, SUM OF 2 ANGLES, DIFFERENCE OF 2 ANGLES

In the past, I would have just listed the following formulas. But very recently, a student has shown me it is necessary to derive at least the first formula for belief. Believing a formula is true somehow makes it easier to learn. I don't know why, but it does to many students. We will derive the cos (A − B). We need to use the unit circle, that is, the circle $x^2 + y^2 = 1$, the circle center at the origin, r = 1. On this circle cos A = x/r, but r = 1. So x = cos A. sin A = y/r = y/1 = y. So y = sin A. So every point (x,y) on the unit circle is given by (cos A,sin A), as in the first figure here. Aren't mathematicians clever?!

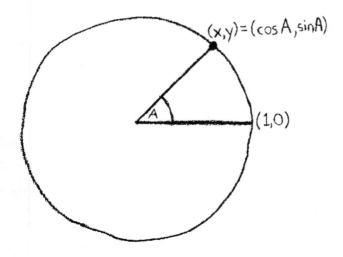

On the second circle, we draw the angles A,B, and A − B. We label the points on the circle as we did in the first picture. We draw the chords. We learned in geometry that in a circle, if there are equal central angles (both A − B), there are equal chords. Chord lengths mean the distance formula. We will use the square of the distance formulas so that there are no square roots.

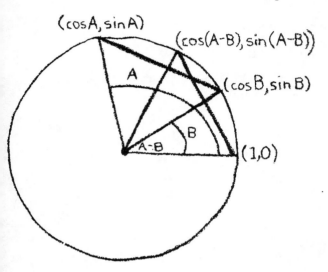

$$(x_2 - x_1)^2 + (y_2 - y_1)^2 = (x_4 - x_3)^2 + (y_4 - y_3)^2$$

$$[\cos(A - B) - 1]^2 + [\sin(A - B) - 0]^2$$

$$= (\cos A - \cos B)^2 + (\sin A - \sin B)^2$$

We just multiply it out, and that will be the answer.

$$\sin^2(A - B) + \cos^2(A - B) - 2\cos(A - B) + 1$$

$$= \sin^2 A + \cos^2 A + \sin^2 B + \cos^2 B$$

$$- 2(\cos A)(\cos B) - 2(\sin A)(\sin B)$$

$$1 - 2\cos(A - B) + 1 = 1 + 1 - 2(\cos A)(\cos B) - 2(\sin A)(\sin B)$$

$\sin^2 + \cos^2$ of 3 different angles is 1

$$2 - 2\cos(A - B) = 2 - 2(\cos A)(\cos B) - 2(\sin A)(\sin B)$$

The reason? 1 + 1 = 2. I love to say that in an advanced class. Now subtract 2 from both sides and divide everything by −2

$$\cos(A - B) = \cos A \cos B + \sin A \sin B$$

I hope you will trust me for the rest of the formulas. They are derived in virtually every trig book. The reasons I derived this one are 2: too many people think to find the cos (A − B), you use the distributive law; and some others can't imagine why a formula like $\cos(A - B)$ requires knowing the sines as well as the cosines. I hope you are convinced.

Here is the second list of identities. In order to be very good, you should memorize this list, even if your instructor tells you you do not have to.

$\cos(A - B) = \cos A \cos B + \sin A \sin B$ $\cos(A + B) = \cos A \cos B - \sin A \sin B$

$\sin(A - B) = \sin A \cos B - \cos A \sin B$ $\sin(A + B) = \sin A \cos B + \cos A \sin B$

$\tan(A - B) = \dfrac{\tan A - \tan B}{1 + \tan A \tan B}$ $\tan(A + B) = \dfrac{\tan A + \tan B}{1 - \tan A \tan B}$

Half angle: Precalc, $\cos(A/2) = \pm[(1 + \cos A)/2]^{1/2}$.
   Calc, $\cos^2 A = (1 + \cos 2A)/2$.

Half angle: Precalc, $\sin(A/2) = \pm[(1 - \cos A)/2]^{1/2}$.
   Calc, $\sin^2 A = (1 - \cos 2A)/2$.

Half angle: $\tan(A/2) = \pm[(1 - \cos A)/(1 + \cos A)]^{1/2}$
   $= (1 - \cos A)/\sin A = \sin A/(1 + \cos A)$.

$\cos 2A = \cos^2 A - \sin^2 A = 2\cos^2 A - 1 = 1 - 2\sin^2 A$

$\sin 2A = 2 \sin A \cos A$

$\tan 2A = \dfrac{2 \tan A}{1 - \tan^2 A}$

This third list is a list of identities some of which are nice to know and some of which are not done in every class.

$\sin(90° - A) = \cos A$ $\cos(90° - A) = \sin A$ $\sin(180° - A) = \sin A$

$\sin(-B) = -\sin B$ $\cos(-B) = \cos B$ $\tan(-B) = -\tan B$

$$2 \sin A \cos B = \sin(A + B) + \sin(A - B)$$

$$2 \cos A \sin B = \sin(A + B) - \sin(A - B)$$

$$2 \cos A \cos B = \cos(A + B) + \cos(A - B)$$

$$2 \sin A \sin B = -\cos(A + B) + \cos(A - B)$$

$$\sin C + \sin D = 2 \sin \tfrac{1}{2}(C + D) \cos \tfrac{1}{2}(C - D)$$

$$\sin C - \sin D = 2 \cos \tfrac{1}{2}(C + D) \sin \tfrac{1}{2}(C - D)$$

$$\cos C + \cos D = 2 \cos \tfrac{1}{2}(C + D) \cos \tfrac{1}{2}(C - D)$$

$$\cos C - \cos D = -2 \sin \tfrac{1}{2}(C + D) \sin \tfrac{1}{2}(C - D)$$

In most courses, the majority of the problems are numerical. There are usually a few identities and a few equations. That is what we will do.

EXAMPLE 36   Given $\cos A = 4/5$ in IV and $\sin B = -5/13$ in III.
Find $\sin 2B$, $\cos 2A$, $\tan (A - B)$, $\sin (A/2)$, $\cos (A/2)$.

First draw the appropriate triangles. Note 3-4-5 and 5-12-13
Pythagorean triples.

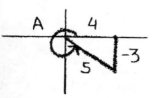 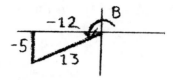

$\sin A = -3/5$, $\cos A = 4/5$, $\tan A = -3/4$. $\sin B = -5/13$, $\cos B = -12/13$, $\tan B = 5/12$.

The first 3, you just plug into the appropriate formula.

a. $\sin 2B = 2 \sin B \cos B = 2(-5/13)(-12/13) = 120/169$

b.   Any of the 3 formulas is OK.
$\cos 2A = \cos^2 A - \sin^2 A = (4/5)^2 - (-3/5)^2 = 7/25$.

c. $\tan (A - B) = \dfrac{\tan A - \tan B}{1 + \tan A \tan B} = \dfrac{(-3/4) - (5/12)}{1 + (-3/4)(5/12)} = -56/33$

For $\sin A/2$ and $\cos A/2$, we use the precalc formulas, but
there is a little more since we have the $\pm$ sign. We would like to
know which sign. Since A is in IV, $270° < A < 360°$. So $135° < A/2 < 180°$, dividing everything by 2. $A/2$ is in the second quadrant.
$\sin (A/2)$ is positive; $\cos (A/2)$ is negative.

$$\sin (A/2) = [(1 - \cos A)/2]^{1/2} = [(1 - 4/5)/2]^{1/2}$$
$$= (1/10)^{1/2} = 10^{1/2}/10$$
$$\cos (A/2) = -[(1 + \cos A)/2]^{1/2} = -[(1 + 4/5)/2]^{1/2}$$
$$= -(9/10)^{1/2} = -3(10)^{1/2}/10$$

EXAMPLE 37   Use 3 different formulas to calculate $\sin 75°$.

a. $\sin (75°) = \sin (45° + 30°) = \sin 45° \cos 30° + \cos 45° \sin 30°$
$$= (2^{1/2}/2)(3^{1/2}/2) + (2^{1/2}/2)(\tfrac{1}{2}) = (6^{1/2} + 2^{1/2})/4$$

b. $\sin (75°) = \sin (120° - 45°) = \sin 120° \cos 45° - \cos 120° \sin 45°$
$$= (3^{1/2}/2)(2^{1/2}/2) - (-\tfrac{1}{2})(2^{1/2}/2) = (6^{1/2} + 2^{1/2})/4$$

c. $\sin (75°) = \sin \tfrac{1}{2}(150°) = [(1 - \cos 150°)/2]^{1/2}$
$$= \frac{[1 - (-3^{1/2}/2)]^{1/2}}{2^{1/2}} = \frac{[1 + (3^{1/2}/2)]^{1/2}}{2^{1/2}}$$

You can use a calculator to check to see that these answers are all the same. It is a very difficult exercise to show the answers are exactly the same. Try it if you are brave. Here's a nasty problem.

EXAMPLE 38   Find sin A if tan 2A = −24/7 in the second quadrant.

If 2A is in II, A is in I.

$$\tan 2A = \frac{2 \tan A}{1 - \tan^2 A} = \frac{-24}{7}$$ **Cross multiply—**
−24(1 − tan² A) = 14 tan A

Rearranging, we get 24 tan² A − 14 tan A − 24 = 0 or 2(3 tan A − 4)(4 tan A + 3) = 0. tan A = −3/4—extraneous since A in I. tan A = 4/3. So sin A = 4/5. (A 3-4-5 triangle.)

EXAMPLE 39   Show sin (180° − A) = sin A. This is just a hammer-it-out identity. sin (180° − A) = (sin 180°)(cos A) − (cos 180°)(sin A) = sin A since sin 180° = 0 and cos 180° = −1.

Since sin 180° = 0 and cos 180° = −1.

EXAMPLE 40   sin (A + B) − sin (A − B) = 2 cos A sin B. Another hammer-it-out.

sin (A + B) − sin (A − B) = sin A cos B + cos A sin B

$$- (\sin A)(\cos B) + (\cos A)(\sin B)$$

$$= 2 \cos A \sin B$$

EXAMPLE 41   Show sin 3A = 3 sin A − 4 sin³ A. This is a little more work.

sin 3A = sin (2A + A) = sin 2A cos A + cos 2A sin A

$$= 2(\sin A)(\cos A)(\cos A) + (1 - 2 \sin^2 A)(\sin A)$$

$$= 2 \sin (1 - \sin^2 A) + (1 - 2 \sin^2 A)(\sin A) = 3 \sin A - 4 \sin^3 A$$

In some places you have to know this one too!!!!!

In doing equations involving double or triple angles, there are two basic types: one where the double (triple) angle goes and one where it stays.

EXAMPLE 42   cos 2x + sin x = 0. Trig substitute for cos 2x, the one involving sin x.

$(1 - 2 \sin^2 x) + \sin x = 0$ or $-2 \sin^2 x + \sin x + 1 = 0$

or $-1(2 \sin x + 1)(\sin x - 1) = 0$

We've done these many times before (the more you do, the better you get). $\sin x = -\frac{1}{2}$ or 1. So $x = 210°, 330°, 90°$ or $7\pi/6, 11\pi/6, \pi/2$. (If you forget, always draw the triangles!!!!!)

The other type (there could be combinations of this with the last type) is where the multiple angle stays. The techniques are the same as in the first section on identities. So we'll just do a basic one.

EXAMPLE 43 $\sin(3A) = \frac{1}{2}$. If $0 \leq A \leq 360°$, then $0 \leq 3A \leq 1080°$. Since the sine is periodic, period 360°, we must add 360° to each 3A angle as long as the total is less than 1080°, so that when we divide by 3, all the angles are between 0° and 360°. $3A = 30°, 150°$; $30° + 360°, 150° + 360°$; $30° + 720°, 150° + 720°$. $3A = 30°, 150°, 390°, 510°, 750°, 870°$. So $A = 10°, 50°, 130°, 170°, 250°, 290°$.

Note 1: If you add 360° too many times, when you divide by 3, the answer will be more than 360°.

Note 2: If our example were $\sin 9A$, you'd add 360° EIGHT times to each angle in the answer.

INVERSE TRIG FUNCTIONS

One of the things that amazes me is how often inverse trig functions are taught without understanding inverse functions. If you have forgotten, review inverse functions, which are in Chapter 9.

If you recall, there must be a $1 - 1$ correspondence between domain and range—usually indicated by a function that increases only or decreases only. As you see, $y = \sin x$ does not fit this description.

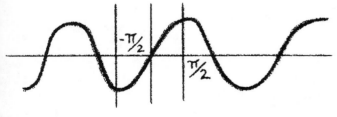

We have to restrict the original domain, as pictured. So the only angles we consider are $-\pi/2 \leq x \leq \pi/2$. Remember this!!!!!!!

Definition: arc sin x or inverse sin (notation arc sin x or $\sin^{-1} x$)

Domain $-1 \leq x \leq 1$ range $-\pi/2 \leq y \leq \pi/2$

Define: arc sin x = y if originally sin y = x.

EXAMPLE 44   Find the arc sin $\frac{1}{2}$ (read, "We are looking for the angle whose sine is $\frac{1}{2}$").

Since the arc sine is defined in the first and fourth quadrants only—first, positive angles, and fourth, negative angles—*the only answer is $\pi/6$ since sin $(\pi/6) = \frac{1}{2}$ and $\pi/6$ is in the first quadrant.*

EXAMPLE 45 $\sin^{-1}(-1/2^{1/2})$

The answer must be in IV and a negative angle. Answer: $-\pi/4$.

In most schools, one discusses arc sin, arc cos, and arc tan. We will too. You should learn this chart!!!!!

Trig Function	Domain	Range
$\sin^{-1}$	$-1 \leq x \leq 1$	$-\pi/2 \leq y \leq \pi/2$
$\cos^{-1}$	$-1 \leq x \leq 1$	$0 \leq y \leq \pi$
$\tan^{-1}$	$-\infty < x < \infty$	$-\pi/2 < y < \pi/2$

EXAMPLE 46   a. $\tan^{-1} 1$.   b. $\tan^{-1}(-1/3^{1/2})$.

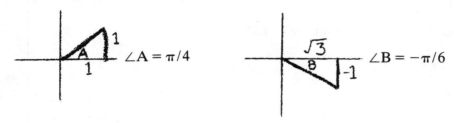

EXAMPLE 47   a. $\cos^{-1}\frac{1}{2}$.   b. $\cos^{-1}(-3^{1/2}/2)$.

Remember: arc sin and arc tan are in quadrants I and IV; arc cos is in I and II.

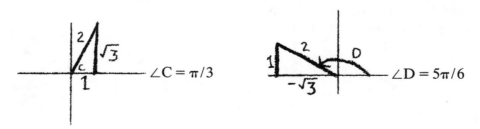

EXAMPLE 48   sec (arc tan 5/7). We are looking for the secant of the angle whose tangent is 5/7.

Draw a triangle whose tangent is 5/7 in I. Find the third side and then get the secant which is r/x. $r = (7^2 + 5^2)^{1/2} = 74^{1/2}$. The secant is $74^{1/2}/7$.

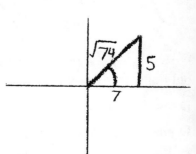

EXAMPLE 49   cot $(\sin^{-1} v)$. We are looking for the cotangent of the angle whose sine is $v = v/1$.

Draw the triangle. $\sin = y/r = v/1$. $x = (1-v^2)^{1/2}$. cot is $x/y = (1-v^2)^{1/2}/v$. This is used in calc. It is not hard with a little practice. In fact it is more fun with letters.

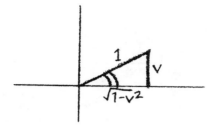

EXAMPLE 50 $\sin(\cos^{-1} p + \sin^{-1} q)$. Let $A = \cos^{-1} p$ and $B = \sin^{-1} q$. So $\cos A = p$ and $\sin B = q$.

Draw both triangles. We are looking for $\sin(A + B) = (\sin A)(\cos B) + (\cos A)(\sin B) = (1-p^2)^{1/2}(1-q^2)^{1/2} + pq$.

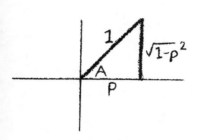
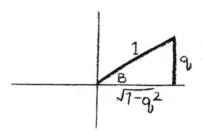

I like these! Hope you will too.

Right-angle trig

If the triangle is in the first quadrant, we can take it out of the x-y plane and look at the triangle a different way.

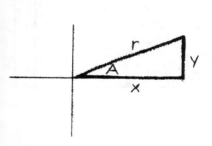
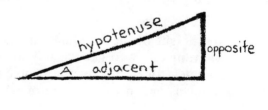

$\sin A = y/r = \text{opposite}/\text{hypotenuse}$ $\cos A = x/r = \text{adjacent}/\text{hypotenuse}$

$\tan A = y/x = \text{opposite}/\text{adjacent}$ $\cot A = x/y = \text{adjacent}/\text{opposite}$

$\sec A = r/x = \text{hypotenuse}/\text{adjacent}$ $\csc A = r/y = \text{hypotenuse}/\text{opposite}$

We could do many, many examples. However most are the same general type. So we will settle for 2 problems: a relatively simple and a relatively complicated one.

In some problems, we have the angle of elevation (the angle you look up at) or the angle of depression (the angle you look down at from above). As pictured here they are equal.

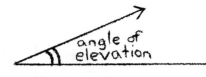

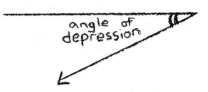

EXAMPLE 51 A man is looking down from the top of a 120-foot lighthouse. The angle of depression to a boat is 20°. How far away is the boat?

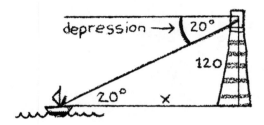

Try to get the variable in the numerator. $\cot 20° = x/120$. So $x = 120 \cot 20°$. Calculator: 20, tan, 1/x, *, 120, =. Answer is 330 feet.

EXAMPLE 52 John is 200 feet from a building on which is located a tall antenna. The angle of elevation to the bottom of the antenna is 70°. The angle of elevation to the top of the antenna is 78°. How tall is the antenna?

There are 2 unknowns: the height of the building and the height of the antenna. We always want to try to get the unknown we don't want (the building) in the numerator. It makes the problem easier. In this problem, both unknowns are in the numerator when you use tangent.

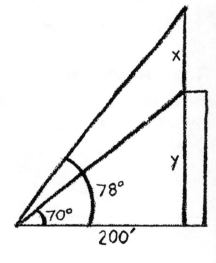

$$\tan 78° = (x + y)/200 \qquad x + y = 200 \tan 78°$$

$$\tan 70° = y/200 \qquad\qquad y = 200 \tan 70° \qquad \textbf{Subtract; factor}$$

$$x = 200(\tan 78° - \tan 70°) = 394 \text{ feet} \quad \text{(big!)}$$

THE LAW OF SINES

When we don't have a right angle, we must use the law of sines or the law of cosines.

Definition LAW OF SINES — $a/\sin A = b/\sin B = c/\sin C$. **Note:** Side is small letter; angle opposite is the same letter, only capitalized.

For this exercise we will say sin 45° = .7, which is approximately correct.

We use the law of sines whenever we have any 2 angles and a side or 2 sides and an angle opposite 1 of those sides.

Two angles and a side

If we have 2 angles, we have the third angle. With a side, we learned, in geometry, that triangles are congruent by angle, side, angle. Therefore 1 solution is possible.

EXAMPLE 53 A = 56°, B = 73°, and a = 20. Find all the other parts. C = 180° − (56° + 73°) = 51°. a/sin A = b/sin B. 20/sin 56° = b/sin 73°. b = 20 sin 73°/sin 56°. b = 263. a/sin A = c/sin C. 20/sin 56° = c/sin 51°. c = 20 sin 51°/sin 56°. c = 19.

Two sides and an angle opposite one of those sides

If you draw the triangle, we have side, side, angle. From geometry, we know triangles are *not* congruent. This is called the ambiguous case. No, 1 or 2 triangles are possible. Let us give 1 example of each.

EXAMPLE 54 Let a = 10, A = 30°, b = 50. a/sin A = b/sin B. 10/sin 30 = 50/sin B. sin B = (50 sin 30)/10 = 2.5. No triangle, since the sine is never bigger than 1.

EXAMPLE 55 A = 135°, a = 70, b = 50. a/sin A = b/sin B. 70/sin 135° = 50/sin B. sin B = (50 sin 135)/70. sin B = $\frac{1}{2}$. B = 30° or 180° − 30° = 150°.

135° + 30° = 165° is OK. 135° + 150° = 285° is no good—sum of angles of a triangle is 180°. One triangle is possible. A = 135°, B = 30°, so C = 15°. a = 70, b = 50. a/sin A = c/sin C. 70/sin 135° = c/sin 15°. c = 70 sin 15°/sin 135°. c = 26.

EXAMPLE 56 C = 30°. c = 5. d = 7. c/sin C = d/sin D. 5/sin 30 = 7/sin D. sin D = (7 sin 30°)/5 = .7. D = 45° or D′ = 180 − 45 = 135°. 30 + 45, OK. 30 + 135 OK. 2 triangles!!!

Triangle 1. C = 30°, D = 45°, E = 105°. c = 5, d = 7, e/sin 105° = 5/sin 30°. e = 9.7.

Triangle 2. C = 30°, D′ = 135°, E′ = 15°. c = 5, d = 7, e′/sin 15° = 5/sin 30°. e′ = 2.6.

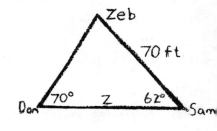

EXAMPLE 57   The angle between Zeb and Sam as seen by Don is 70°. The angle between Don and Zeb as seen by Sam is 62°. Zeb and Sam are 70 feet apart. How far apart are Don and Sam?

Angle at Zeb is 48°. z/sin 48° = 70/sin 70°. z = 55 feet.

THE LAW OF COSINES

We use the law of cosines whenever we have 3 sides or 2 sides and the included angle.

Definition   LAW OF COSINES — $c^2 = a^2 + b^2 - 2ab \cos C$. Again note angle C opposite side c. In each case only 1 triangle possible since triangles are congruent by side, side, side or side, angle, side.

EXAMPLE 58   a = 3, b = 5, c = 7. $c^2 = a^2 + b^2 - 2ab \cos C$. $7^2 = 3^2 + 5^2 - 2(3)(5) \cos C$. Careful of the arithmetic. $15 = -30 \cos C$. $\cos C = -\frac{1}{2}$. C = 120° (quadrant II).

Note: Whenever you have 4 parts of a triangle, it is easier to use the law of sines. 3/sin A = 7/sin 120°. A = 22°. B = 180° − (22 + 120) = 38°.

EXAMPLE 59   x = 10, y = 20, Z = 40°. $z^2 = x^2 + y^2 - 2xy \cos Z$. $z^2 = 10^2 + 20^2 - 2(10)(20) \cos 40°$. z = 13.9. 13.9/sin 40° = 10/sin X. sin X = 10(sin 40°)/13.9. X = $\sin^{-1}$ (10 sin 40°/13.9). X = 28°. Y = 180° − (28° + 40°) = 112°.

EXAMPLE 60   A plane travels east for 200 miles. It turns at a 25° angle to the north for 130 miles. How many miles from home is the plane?

$$x^2 = 200^2 + 130^2 - 2(200)(130) \cos 155°$$

x = 323 miles

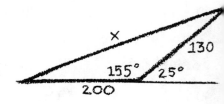

I hope this chapter is sufficient to give you a thorough knowledge of trig. If you do get this knowledge it will more than prepare you for calculus.

11. CURVE SKETCHING

As I've said in my other books, this is the topic I teach better than anyone else in the world. After reading this chapter, you will be nearly as good. This chapter will be written in a slightly different order than the discussion of curve sketching in the calc book. Of course the part that requires calculus has been omitted here.

POLYNOMIALS

We will sketch polynomials looking only at intercepts and the exponents of x-intercepts. With just a little practice, you will become lightning fast. First let's look at the individual cases.

EXAMPLE 1 $y = 6(x - 3)^8$

We want to look at this around its x-intercept. We ignore the exponent and see the intercept is (3,0). We would like to see it a little to the right of 3, at 3^+, and to the left of 3, at 3^-. Remember 3^+ means 3.000001 and 3^- means 2.999999. When we substitute, we are NOT interested in the answer but only the SIGN OF THE ANSWER to see if a nearby point is above or below the x-axis. Point A: $x = 3^+$. $3^+ - 3$ is positive. Positive to the 8th power is positive. Six times a positive number is positive. Point A is above the x-axis. Let B have $x = 3^-$. $3^- - 3$ is negative. A negative to the 8th power (even power) is POSITIVE. Six times a positive is positive. B is also above the x-axis.

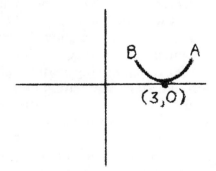

EXAMPLE 2 $y = -5(x - 4)^{88}$

Intercept (4,0). A: $x = 4^+$. $4^+ - 4$ is positive. Positive to the 88th power is positive; -5 times a positive is negative. Point A is below the x-axis. For B, $x = 4^-$. 4^- –4 is negative. Negative to the 88th power is positive; –5 times a positive is again negative.

To summarize, if you have an even power, the curve does NOT cross at the intercept.

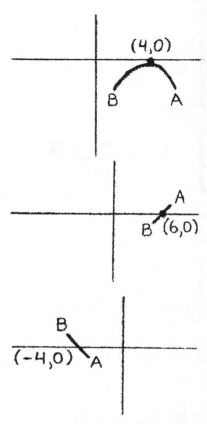

EXAMPLE 3 $y = 9(x - 6)^5$

Intercept (6,0). A: $x = 6^+$. y is positive. A is above the x-axis. B: $x = 6^-$. $6^- - 6$ is negative. Negative to the 5th power (odd) is negative; 9 times a negative is negative. B is below the x-axis.

EXAMPLE 4 $y = -8(x + 4)^7$

Intercept (–4,0). A: $x = (-4)^+$. $(-4)^+ = -3.999999999$. $(-4)^+ + 4$ is positive. Positive to the 7th power is positive. Positive times (–8) is negative. (That is point A.) Point A is below the x-axis. B, $x = (-4)^-$. $(-4)^- + 4$ is negative. Negative to the 7th power is negative; –8 times a negative is positive. B is above the x-axis.

In summary, if the exponent is ODD, there IS a crossing at the x-intercept.

Note: If $y = 4(x - 3)$, the exponent of (x – 3) is 1, which is odd. So there would be a crossing at (3,0).

EXAMPLE 5 $y = (x - 1)^2(x - 2)(x - 5)$

x-intercepts whenever y = 0. (1,0),(2,0)(5,0). y-intercept at x = 0. We must substitute x = 0. $y = (0 - 1)^2(0 - 2)(0 - 5) = 10$. (0,10). We must substitute 1 number to tell us where the graph starts. That number is to the right of the rightmost intercept. In this case x = 5.1. $(5.1 - 1)^2(5.1 - 2)(5.1 - 5)$ is positive, so the point is above the x-axis. REMEMBER, we care about the sign only. The power of (x – 5) is 1, which is odd. So it crosses at (5,0), and the point is below the x-axis when we near (2,0). The power of (x – 2) is odd, and the crossing is under to above as we near (1,0). $(x - 1)^2$ term has power 2, which is even. The graph is above to the right. So it is above to the left. The curve goes through (0,10). Both ends head to plus infinity, since there are no other x-intercepts, and to the right of (5,0) and to the left of (1,0) the graph is above the x-axis. The sketch looks as shown here.

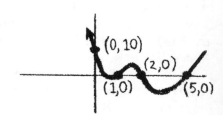

With a little practice, you will see how quick this can get. Let us give a very easy example.

EXAMPLE 5 $y = x^3 - 2x^2 - 8x$

Factor $y = x(x - 4)(x + 2)$. Intercepts are (0,0),(4,0),(–2,0).

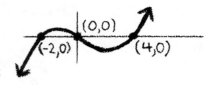

Substitute x = 4.1 in factored form. You will see y is positive. To the right of (x − 4), the sketch is above the x-axis. All the exponents are odd. So the sketch goes cross, cross, cross.

   Note: If we have the intercept (0,0), it is an x-intercept, but it is the only y-intercept. We do not have to get y-intercept separately if we have (0,0).   **Also note:** Don't forget (0,0) if it is there.   **Also note:** See how quick this goes: cross, cross, cross.

EXAMPLE 7 $y = (x - 2)^2(3 - x)$

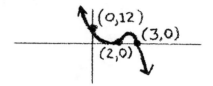

(2,0), (3,0) (careful of this one). x = 0, y = $(-2)^2(3) = 12$. (0,12). x = 3.1 so y = $(3.1 - 2)^2(3 - 3.1)$ is negative. So the curve starts below the x-axis, with the right end going to minus infinity. The power of (3 − x) is odd. So there is a crossing from below to above. At (2,0), the power is even—$(x - 2)^2$—so the graph stays above the x-axis at (2,0), goes through (0,12), and heads to plus infinity. It looks as shown here.

EXAMPLE 8   Let us take a mean-looking one and show how really easy it is. $y = x^3(x - 2)^4(x - 4)^5(x - 6)^6(x - 8)^7$. Intercepts (0,0),(2,0), (4,0),(6,0),(8,0). Substitute x = 8.1. y is positive. To the right of (8,0) above. Right end goes to plus infinity.

   $(x - 8)^7$, power is odd. Crossing above to below.

   $(x - 6)^6$, power is even. There is no crossing. Graph stays below.

   $(x - 4)^5$, power is odd. Crossing is below to above. Remember we
      always go from right to left.

   $(x - 2)^4$, power is even. There is no crossing. Sketch stays above the
      x-axis.

   x^3, power is odd. Crossing is above to below, and the right end goes
      to minus infinity.

Its sketch is as shown here.

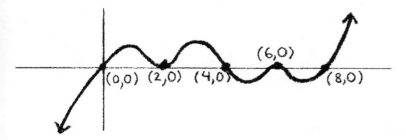

With a little practice you WILL do these in no time at all.

RATIONAL FUNCTIONS

We are next going to sketch rational functions—which are polynomials divided by polynomials. The intercept part is exactly the same. We need to introduce the concept of ASYMPTOTE. For our purposes, an asymptote is a line to which a graph gets very close "at the end" but never hits.

You may have been told that a curve cannot hit an asymptote. That is not true. An asymptote is a straight-line approximation when either x or y goes to plus or minus infinity. "In the middle of the graph," the curve is not a straight line. So the graph may hit the asymptote a number of times. At the end, though, the curve cannot hit it. Shown here is an example.

The x-axis is the asymptote; the axis is hit 4 times, but not at the end.

Recall: The DEGREE of a polynomial in 1 unknown is its highest exponent. The degree of $y = 7x^4 - 9x^5 + 3x + 2$ is 5.

Vertical asymptotes

The vertical asymptotes are lines. They are gotten by setting the bottom of the fraction equal to zero.

Note 1: Polynomials have no denominators. Therefore, they have no asymptotes of any kind.

Note 2: The discussion of vertical asymptotes is very similar to that of intercepts.

EXAMPLE 9 $y = \dfrac{4}{(x-6)^8}$

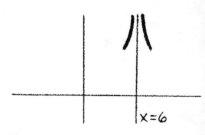

Vertical asymptote at $x = 6$. If we substitute $6^+, 6^-$ as before, y is positive. So on both sides of $x = 6$, the curve goes to plus infinity. The picture would look as shown here.

EXAMPLE 10 $\quad y = \dfrac{-3}{(x-4)^{22}}$

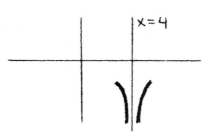

Vertical asymptote at x = 4. When you substitute $4^+, 4^-$—you can use 4.1 and 3.9—the value of y is negative. Both ends go to minus infinity. Again the curve looks as shown here.

To summarize, if a term has an even exponent in the BOTTOM, both ends of the curve either go to plus infinity or go to minus infinity.

EXAMPLE 11 $\quad y = 7/(x-9)^5$

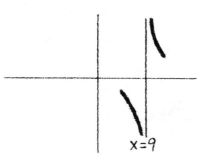

Vertical asymptote at x = 9. If we substitute 9.1, y is positive, and the right side of x = 9 goes to plus infinity. If we substitute x = 8.9, the value of y is negative. The left side goes to minus infinity. The picture is as shown here.

EXAMPLE 12 $\quad y = -8/x - 3$

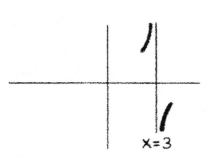

Vertical asymptote at x = 3. Remember x = 3, power is 1; which is odd. x = 3.1, y is negative. To the right the curve goes to minus infinity (down). x = 2.9, y is positive, to the left the curve goes to plus infinity (up). The picture is again as shown here.

To summarize, if we have an odd exponent in the bottom, 1 end goes to plus infinity (up) and the other end (on the other side of the asymptote), goes to minus infinity (down).

Horizontal asymptotes

There are two types of horizontal asymptotes.

Suppose y = P(x)/Q(x). The degree of the top is less than the degree of the bottom. We always get the horizontal asymptote y = 0, the x-axis. Let us verify this for 1 example.

EXAMPLE 13
$$y = \frac{5x^2 + 8x}{4 + 9x^3}$$

The degree of the top is 2; the degree of the bottom is 3. The degree of the bottom is bigger. Horiz. asymp. is y = 0. Let us verify. Divide top and bottom by x^3. This is OK since x goes to $\pm\infty$ and not to 0. We get . . .

$$y = \frac{5/x + 8/x^2}{4/x^3 + 9}$$

$5/x$, $8/x^2$, $4/x^3$ all go to 0 as x goes to ±infinity. So $y \to 0/9 = 0$, as promised. In the future do not do the work. If the bottom degree is bigger, $y = 0$ will always be the horizontal asymptote

Suppose the degree of the top is the same as the bottom; the horizontal asymptote is

$$y = \frac{a}{b}$$ a is the coefficient of the highest power on top
b is the coefficient of the highest power on the bottom

EXAMPLE 14

$$y = \frac{5x^3 + 7x^2}{4 - 9x^3}$$

Degree of top and bottom is 3. The asymptote is $y = 5/(-9)$. Again let us verify, so that you believe. Divide by x^3

$$y = \frac{5 + 7/x}{4/x^3 - 9}$$

$7/x$ and $4/x^3$ go to 0 as x goes to ± infinity. So $y \to -(5/9)$

An oblique asymptote occurs when the degree of the top is 1 more than the bottom. In order to get it we long divide the bottom into the top. Groan, "Aarrgh!"

EXAMPLE 15 $y = \dfrac{x^2 - 4x + 4}{x - 1}$

$$
\begin{array}{r}
x \quad -3 \ + 1/(x-1) \\
x - 1 \overline{)\ x^2 - 4x + 4} \\
\underline{x^2 - x} \\
-3x + 4 \\
\underline{-3x + 3} \\
1
\end{array}
$$

The remainder $1/x - 1$ goes to 0 as x goes to ± infinity. The oblique (slanted) asymptote is $y = x - 3$.

Note: If the degree of the top is more than 1 more than the bottom, there are no horizontal or oblique asymptotes.

Also note: There is at most 1 horizontal or 1 oblique asymptote when you sketch rational functions. There might be none. There cannot be 1 of each.

EXAMPLE 16 $y = \dfrac{(x - 1)^4(x + 2)^3}{(x + 1)^8(x - 2)^1}$

Now don't panic. Pretty soon you will be able to do this in less than 2 minutes. We do this very systematically.

x-intercept y = 0, top of the fraction = 0. (1,0) and (−2,0).

y-intercept x = 0, y = $(-1)^4(2)^3/1^8(-2)^1 = -4$. (0,−4).

Vertical asymptotes, bottom = 0. x = −1, x = 2.

Horizontal asymptote: Degree of top is 7 (if we multiplied out the top, and we wouldn't really do it on the grounds of sanity, the highest power is x^7, the only term we are interested in); the degree of the bottom is 9. Since the degree of the bottom is bigger, we get *y = 0, the x-axis.*

We start the sketch. We always start from the rightmost x-intercept or rightmost vertical asymptote. In this case we start at x = 2, the vertical asymptote. We substitute x = 2.1 and find that y will be a positive number. So the curve goes to plus infinity on the right side of x = 2.

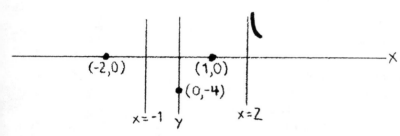

To continue the sketch, the power of (x − 2) is 1, an odd number. Since the right side went to plus infinity, the left side must go to minus infinity. We come up to the point (1,0). $(x - 1)^4$ is an even exponent. So there is no crossing. The curve stays below, goes through (0,−4), and heads to minus infinity at x = −1.

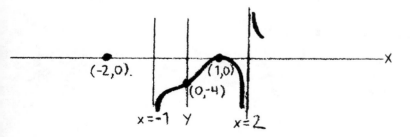

At $(x + 1)^8$, the power is even. Both ends are in the same location. In this case both ends are at minus infinity. The left side heads up to (−2,0). $(x + 2)^3$ has an odd power. So there is a crossing. Both ends head toward the horizontal asymptote, y = 0, the x-axis. **DON'T FORGET THE ENDS!!!!!**

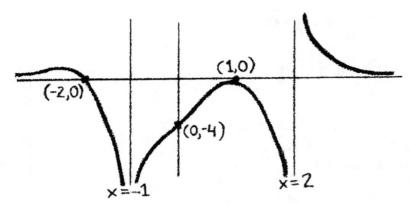

That's it. Again do not panic. You will get it easily if you go over this example and the next few several times.

EXAMPLE 17 $y = \dfrac{2x^3}{(x-3)^2(x-1)}$ $y = \dfrac{2x^3}{x^3 + \cdots}$

x-intercept y = 0, x = 0. (0,0) only x and y intercept.

Vertical asymptotes x = 1, x = 3.

Horizontal asymptote: Degree top and bottom equal. y = 2/1.

Sketch: Rightmost x = 3. Substitute x = 3.1; everything positive. To the right of x = 3, the curve goes to plus infinity. $(x-3)^2$ has an even power. To the left also goes to plus infinity. The graph comes down and then back up at x = 1 since there are no intercepts between x = 3 and x = 1. The power (x − 1) is odd. Since 1 end is at plus infinity, on the left side, the curve must go to minus infinity. Then we go up to (0,0). Since the power of x^3 is odd, there is a crossing. Both ends go to the horizontal asymptote, y = 2. The sketch is here.

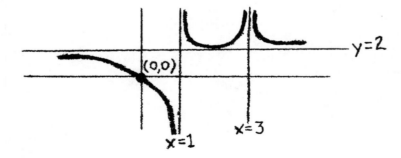

EXAMPLE 18 $y = \dfrac{x^2 - 4x + 4}{x - 1} = \dfrac{(x-2)^2}{x-1} = x - 3 + 1/(x-1)$

When the degree of the top is 1 more than the bottom, we need 3 forms: the original, the factored form (if possible), and the long divided form.

x-intercept (from factored form) (2,0).

y-intercept x = 0 in original (0,−4).

Vertical asymptote x = 1. No horiz. asymp.

Oblique asymptote y = x − 3 (graph this in any way you know how).

Sketch: Use factored form: $(x-2)^4$. Substitute x = 2.1 into everything. y positive. Power is even. Both ends are above intercept (2,0), no cross. Head for x = 1. Right end must go to plus infinity. Since the power of x − 1 is odd, the other end goes to minus infinity. It then heads up to the point (0,−4). The very ends of the graph go to the line y = x − 3. The sketch is as shown here.

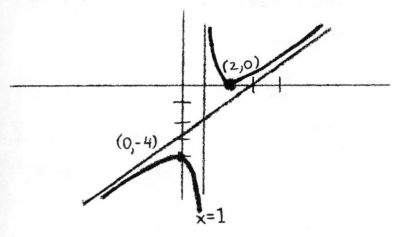

EXAMPLE 19 $y = \dfrac{x^8}{(x+3)^5} = \dfrac{x^8}{x^5 + \cdots} = \text{approx. } x^3$

Intercept (0,0).

Vertical asymptote x = −3.

Since the degree of the top is more than 1 more than the bottom, there are no horizontal or oblique asymptotes. However we would like to know what happens to the ends. At the ends the curve is approximately x^3. Substitute a big number, x = 100. $(100)^3$ positive. Right end goes to plus infinity. Substitute a small number, x = −100. $(-100)^3$ negative. Left end goes to minus infinity.

Let's do the middle (really should be done first). (0,0) is the rightmost. Letting x = .1, we again get y positive. As we now know, the right end goes to plus infinity. Since the power of x^8 is even, there is no crossing. The left end goes positive up to plus infinity at x = −3. Since the power of $(x+3)^5$ is odd and the right side goes to plus infinity, the left side goes to minus infinity. The curve gets bigger for a while, and then it turns around and heads for minus infinity again. Its sketch is on the next page.

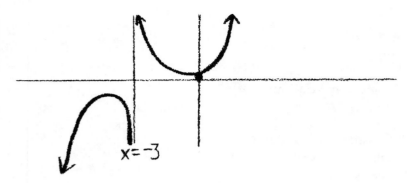

If you go through this, you will understand curve sketching and do it faster than your teacher.

This is the end of the second section on functions. There is another large important one, but first . . . .

12. MODERN LOGARITHMS

We will do a modern approach to logs. Modern to a mathematician means not more than 50 years behind the times. We will not do calculations with logs (calculations involving characteristics and mantissas). This is no longer needed because we have calculators. What is needed is a thorough understanding of the laws of logarithms and certain problems that can only be solved with logs.

Definition $\log_b x = y$ (log of x to the base b is y) if $b^y = x$.

Note: y, the answer, which is also the log itself, is an exponent ($b^y = x$). The laws of logarithms are the laws of exponents, as we will see.

EXAMPLE 1   Show $\log_5 25 = 2$ is true. Using the definition, $\log_5 25 = 2$ means $5^2 = 25$.

EXAMPLE 2   Write $4^3 = 64$ in log form. Base 4, exponent 3, answer 64. So we get $\log_4 64 = 3$.

Note: This definition must be practiced!!!!!

EXAMPLE 3   Find $\log_{16} 64$. Let $\log_{16} 64 = x$. Use the definition of log since this is all we know at this point.

$$16^x = 64 \qquad (2^4)^x = 2^6 \qquad 2^{4x} = 2^6$$

Since the bases are equal, the exponents are equal. $4x = 6$. $x = 3/2$.

EXAMPLE 4   Solve for x: $\log_9 x = -3/2$. $9^{-3/2} = x$. (Review fractional exponents.)

$$x = 9^{-3/2} = 1/9^{3/2} = 1/(9^{1/2})^3 = 1/3^3 = 1/27$$

EXAMPLE 5   Solve for x: $\log_x 32 = 5$. $x^5 = 32$. So $x = 32^{1/5}$. $x = 2$.

We will now discuss what the base can be and the domain and range of logs.

BASE: Can the base be negative? No, since $(-2)^{1/2}$ is imaginary. Can the base be 0? No, since 0^n is either 0 or undefined (if n is 0 or negative). Are there any other exclusions? Yes. b cannot be 1, since 1^n always is 1.

The base can be any positive number other than 1. The base could be $2^{1/2}$, but it won't do you much good since there are no tables or calculators for it. The 2 most common bases are 10, since we have 10 fingers, and e, a number that comes up a lot, later in math.

1.   e is approx. 2.7. More exactly? On your calculator press 1, inv, 1n.

2. $\log_{10} = \log$.

3. $\log_e = \ln$ (ln is called the natural logarithm).

Definition   RANGE OF LOGS (the y values) — A log, y, is an exponent. Exponents can be positive, zero, and negative. The range is all real numbers.

Definition   DOMAIN OF LOGS (the x values) — Since the base is positive, whether the exponent is positive, zero, or negative, the answer x will always be positive. So the domain is all numbers bigger than zero. (Remember—"negative exponent" means reciprocal.)

LAW 1 $\log_b xy = \log_b x + \log_b y$

EXAMPLE 6 $\log 6 = \log (2)(3) = \log 2 + \log 3$

LAW 2 $\log_b (m/n) = \log_b m - \log_b n$

EXAMPLE 7 $\log (4/3) = \log 4 - \log 3$

LAW 3 $\log_b x^p = p \log_b x$

EXAMPLE 8 $\log 32 = \log 2^5 = 5 \log 2$

These 3 laws are the most important. In calculus if you can do the next problem, you know 50% of what you need.

EXAMPLE 9 Simplify with no exponents: $\ln\left(\dfrac{a^4\sqrt{b}}{c^6 d^7}\right)$.

Add all the logs on the top, subtract all the logs on the bottom, and exponents come down and multiply the specific log.

Answer: $4\ln a + \frac{1}{2}\ln b - 6\ln c - 7\ln d$

EXAMPLE 10 Write as a single log:
$5\log h - 7\log c - 8\log p - 4\log j + (3/4)\log k + \log v$.

Everything with a plus sign is multiplied in the numerator; everything with a minus sign is multiplied in the denominator; coefficients come up as exponents.

Answer: $\log\left(\dfrac{h^5 k^{3/4} v}{c^7 p^8 j^4}\right)$

LAW 4 $\log_b b = 1$ since $b^1 = b$. $\log_7 7 = \log 10 = \ln e = 1$.

LAW 5 $\log_b 1 = 0$ since $b^0 = 1$. $\log_9 1 = \log 1 = \ln 1 = 0$.

LAW 6 The log is an increasing function. If $m < n$, then $\log m < \log n$. We know $\log 2 < \log 3$ since $2 < 3$.

LAW 7 The log is $1 - 1$. That is, if $\log_b x = \log_b y$, then $x = y$.

EXAMPLE 11 $\log_5(x^{1/2}) = \log_5(2x - 3)$. By $1 - 1$

$$x^{1/2} = 2x - 3$$ We must square both sides. In doing this we might introduce extraneous solutions. We must check them back in the original equation

$$(x^{1/2})^2 = (2x - 3)^2 \quad \text{or} \quad x = 4x^2 - 12x + 9$$

$$4x^2 - 13x + 9 = 0 \quad \textbf{Now factor}$$

$$(4x - 9)(x - 1) = 0 \quad x = 9/4 \quad \text{or} \quad x = 1$$

Check $x = 9/4$. $\log_5(9/4)^{1/2} \overset{?}{=} \log_5[2(9/4) - 3]$

$\log_5(3/2) = \log_5(3/2)$. Yes, this one checks.

Check x = 1. $\log_5 (1)^{1/2} \overset{?}{=} \log_5 [2(1) - 3]$

$\log_5 1 \neq \log_5 (-1)$ since there is no log of a negative number.

The only solution is x = 9/4.

LAW 8 $b^{\log_b x}$ is a weird way of writing x. $e^{\ln x} = x$.

LAW 9 $\log_b b^x = x$. $\ln e^x = x$.

LAW 10 $\log_d c = \dfrac{\log_b c}{\log_b d}$. $\log_5 7 = \dfrac{\log_{10} 7}{\log_{10} 5}$.

This is LONG division, which of course we don't have to do now since we have calculators.

The following are problems involving logs that you should be able to do.

EXAMPLE 12

$(4) \cdot 3^{x+2} = 28$ **Isolate the exponent. Divide both sides by 4**

$3^{x+2} = 7$ **Now take logs to get x "off the exponent"**

$(x + 2) \log 3 = \log 7$ **At this point, this is an elementary algebra problem. You must solve for x. Remember log 3 and log 7 are numbers**

$x \log 3 + 2 \log 3 = \log 7$

$x = \dfrac{\log 7 - 2 \log 3}{\log 3}$ **Using a calculator we get x = −.23**

EXAMPLE 13

$5^{3x-6} = 7^{8x+9}$ **Take logs**

$(3x - 6) \log 5 = (8x + 9) \log 7$

$3x \log 5 - 6 \log 5 = 8x \log 7 + 9 \log 7$

$3x \log 5 - 8x \log 7 = 6 \log 5 + 9 \log 7$

$x(3 \log 5 - 8 \log 7) = 6 \log 5 + 9 \log 7$ so $x = \dfrac{6 \log 5 + 9 \log 7}{3 \log 5 - 8 \log 7}$

EXAMPLE 14 $\log_2 x + \log_2 (x - 2) = 3$. $\log m + \log n = \log mn$. Then definition of logs.

$$\log_2 x(x-2) = 3 \quad \text{or} \quad 2^3 = x(x-2) \quad \text{or} \quad x^2 - 2x - 8 = 0$$
$$\text{or} \quad (x-4)(x+2) = 0$$

$x = -2$ rejected, since you cannot take the log of a negative.

$x = 4$ OK, since $\log_2 4 + \log_2 (4-2) = \log_2 4 + \log_2 2 = 2 + 1 = 3$.

EXAMPLE 15 $\log(x-3) - \log 4 = 2$. $\log m - \log n = \log m/n$. Then definition of logs, remembering log means the base is 10.

$\log_{10} (x-3)/4 = 2$ or $(x-3)/4 = 10^2$. $x - 3 = 400$. So $x = 403$. Not too bad, is it?

EXAMPLE 16 Sometimes you are given problems involving compound interest. Their formula is given by

$$A = P(1 + r/n)^{nt}$$

where A = amount at the end; P = principal, amount you put in; r = interest rate per year; n = number of times compounded a year; and t = years.

Say we invest \$1000 at 20% interest. If it is compounded 4 times a year, when will we have \$4000?

Problem: $A = 4000$, $P = 1000$, $r = .20$, $n = 4$, $t = ????????$

Solution: Substitute $4000 = 1000(1 + .20/4)^{4t}$. $4000 = 1000(1.05)^{4t}$. Divide by 1000 and take logs.

$$4 = (1.05)^{4t} \quad \log 4 = 4t \log 1.05 \quad t = \frac{\log 4}{4 \log 1.05} \quad t = 7.1 \text{ years}$$

This means in 7.1 years our investment is multiplied by 4. Now if we can only find a 20% safe return!

EXAMPLE 17 If the half life of a radioactive substance is 8 days and we start with 10 pounds of undecayed substance, when will there be 3 pounds of active material left?

In calculus you will derive this. At that time, it will not be hard. Now the formula is $A = A_0(\frac{1}{2})^{t/8}$, where A = amount now, A_0 = amount in the beginning ($t = 0$), t = time, and the denominator of t is the time of the half life.

Let us check the formula: $t = 8$, $A = 10(\frac{1}{2})^{8/8} = 10(\frac{1}{2}) = 5$, one-half as much in 8 days!

Let us do the problem to find out how many days for $A = 3$ pounds left.

$$3 = 10(\tfrac{1}{2})^{t/8}$$ **Divide by 10, take logs, and solve for t**

$.3 = (\tfrac{1}{2})^{t/8}$ $\log .3 = (t/8) \log .5$

$t = (8 \log .3)/\log .5 = 13.9$ days   (by calculator)

If you know these problems, you will be all set not only for precalc but for calc.

13. PARABOLAS II, ELLIPSES, AND HYPERBOLAS

We will now discuss these 3 curves the way they are discussed in calc books and some precalc books.

The important way to study these curves is to relate the equation to the picture. If you do this, this entire chapter will become much easier.

Definition PARABOLA — The set of all points equidistant from a point, called a FOCUS, and a line, called the DIRECTRIX. F is the focus. The point V, the VERTEX, is the closest point to the directrix. **Note:** According to the definition $FV = VR$, $FP_1 = P_1R_1$, $FP_2 = P_2R_2$, etc.

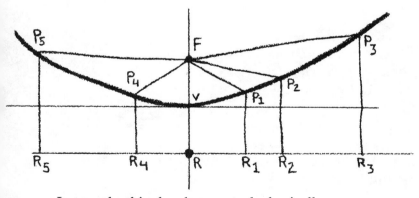

Let us do this development algebraically.

Let the vertex, V, be at (0,0) and focus F, be at (0,c). The directrix is at $y = -c$. Let P(x,y) be any point on the parabola. The definition of the parabola says FP = PQ. Everything on PQ has the same x value, and everything on $y = -c$ has the same y value. Point Q has to be $(x,-c)$. On PQ, since the x values are the same the length of the line is $y - (-c)$. Using the distance formula to get PF and setting the 2 segments squared equal to each other, we get . . . $(x - 0)^2 + (y - c)^2 = (y + c)^2$. Squaring we get $x^2 + y^2 - 2cy + c^2 = y^2 + 2cy + c^2$. Simplifying we get $x^2 = 4cy$.

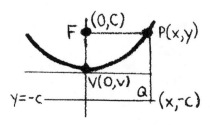

81

Here is a chart that will be helpful in relating the equation to the picture.

Vertex	Focus	Directrix	Equation	Picture	Comment
(0,0)	(0,c)	$y = -c$	$x^2 = 4cy$	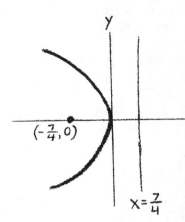	The original derivation
(0,0)	(0,-c)	$y = c$	$x^2 = -4cy$		y replaced by −y
(0,0)	(c,0)	$x = -c$	$y^2 = 4cx$		x,y interchange in top line
(0,0)	(-c,0)	$x = c$	$y^2 = -4cx$		x replaced by −x in the above line

EXAMPLE 1 $y^2 = -7x$. Sketch; label vertex, focus, directrix.

The chart tells us the picture is the last line. Now let 4c equal 7, ignoring the minus sign. c = 7/4. Vertex is (0,0). Focus is (−7/4,0) because it is on the negative x-axis. The directrix is x = +7/4, + because it is to the right and x = 7/4 since it is a vertical line. Easy, isn't it?

EXAMPLE 2 Sketch $(y - 3)^2 = -7(x + 2)$.

To understand this curve, we look at the difference between $x^2 + y^2 = 25$ and $(x - 3)^2 + (y + 6)^2 = 25$. Has the shape changed? No. Has the radius changed? No. The only thing that has changed is its position. The center is now at the point (3,−6) instead of at the point (0,0).

In the case of our little parabola, it is the vertex that has changed. V = (−2,3). (Remember x is always first.) 4c is still equal to 7. c = 7/4, but F is (−2 − 7/4,3), 7/4 to the left of the vertex. The directrix is x = −2 + 7/4. I do not do the arithmetic so that you know where the numbers come from.

EXAMPLE 3 Sketch the parabola $2x^2 + 8x + 6y + 10 = 0$.

$$2x^2 + 8x + 6y + 10 = 0$$

Divide by coefficient of x^2 or y^2

$$x^2 + 4x + 3y + 5 = 0$$

On the left get all the terms related to the square term; everything else on the other side

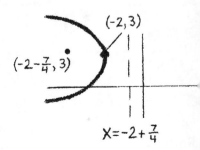

$$x^2 + 4x = -3y - 5$$ **Complete the square; add to both sides**

$$x^2 + 4x + 4 = -3y - 5 + 4$$ **Factor; do the arithmetic**

$$(x + 2)^2 = -3y - 1$$ **Weird last step. No matter what the coefficient on the right, factor it all out, even if it results in a fraction in the parentheses**

$$(x + 2)^2 = -3(y + 1/3)$$

Sketch. Picture just below. $V(-2, -1/3)$. $4c = 3$. $c = 3/4$. $F(-2, -1/3 - 3/4)$. Directrix $y = -1/3 + 3/4$.

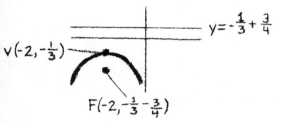

Definition — Algebraically, the ELLIPSE is defined as $PF_1 + PF_2 = 2a$. $2a > 2c$. $2c$ is the distance between the FOCI. a will be determined later. P is any point on the ellipse. To paraphrase the definition, given 2 points called foci, we draw a line from 1 of them to any point on the curve and then from that point on the curve to the other focus; if the sum of the 2 lengths always adds to the same number, $2a$, the figure formed will be an ellipse.

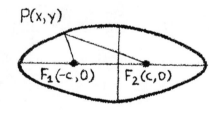

I know you'd all desperately like to draw an ellipse. Take a non-elastic string. Attach thumb tacks at either end. Take a pencil and stretch the string as far as it goes. Go 360°. You will trace an ellipse.

Some of you have seen the equation of an ellipse, but few of you have seen its derivation. It is an excellent algebraic exercise for you to try. You will see there is a lot of algebra behind a very simple equation.

$$PF_1 + PF_2 = 2a$$ **Use the distance formula**

$$\sqrt{(x - (-c))^2 + (y - 0)^2} + \sqrt{(x - c)^2 + (y - 0)^2} = 2a$$ **Isolate 1 square root and square both sides**

$$[\sqrt{(x + c)^2 + y^2}]^2 = [2a - \sqrt{(x - c)^2 + y^2}]^2$$ **Do the algebra**

$$x^2 + 2cx + c^2 + y^2 = 4a^2 + x^2 - 2cx + c^2 + y^2$$
$$- 4a\sqrt{(x-c)^2 + y^2}$$

Combine like terms; isolate the radical

$$4a\sqrt{(x-c)^2 + y^2} = 4a^2 - 4cx$$

Divide by 4; again square both sides

$$[a\sqrt{(x-c)^2 + y^2}]^2 = (4a^2 - 4cx)^2$$

Do the algebra

$$a^2(x^2 - 2cx + c^2 + y^2) = a^4 - 2a^2cx + c^2x^2$$

$$\text{or} \quad a^2x^2 - c^2x^2 + a^2y^2 = a^4 - a^2c^2$$

$$\frac{(a^2 - c^2)x^2}{(a^2 - c^2)a^2} + \frac{a^2y^2}{a^2(a^2 - c^2)} = \frac{a^2(a^2 - c^2)}{a^2(a^2 - c^2)}$$

Factor out x^2 on left 2 terms and a^2 from right 2 terms; divide by $(a^2 - c^2)a^2/2$

We get $\dfrac{x^2}{a^2} + \dfrac{y^2}{a^2 - c^2} = 1$ or $\dfrac{x^2}{a^2} + \dfrac{y^2}{b^2} = 1$, letting $a^2 - c^2 = b^2$. Whew!!!!!!

We are still not finished. Let us find out what a is and b is. $F_1P + PF_2 = 2a$, where P is any point on the ellipse. Let T be the point P. $F_1T + TF_2 = 2a$. By symmetry $F_1T = TF_2$. So $F_1T = TF_2 = a$. Since $a^2 - c^2 = b^2$, $OT = OT' = b$. The coordinates of T are (0,b); T' is (0,-b).

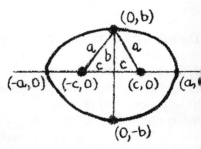

We would like to find the coordinates of U (and U'), but the letters a,b,c are used up. Oh well, let's see what happens. $F_2U + UF_1 = 2a$. $F_2U = x - c$. $UF_1 = x + c$. $x - c + x + c = 2a$. So $2x = 2a$; $x = a$. U is (a,0); U' is (-a,0).

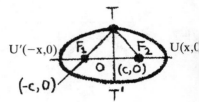

$c = \frac{1}{2}$ the distance between the foci

$b =$ length of the semiminor axis ("semi" means half; "minor" means smaller; "axis" means line)

$a =$ length of semimajor axis = distance from a focus to a minor vertex

$(\pm a,0)$—major vertices

$(0,\pm b)$—minor vertices

$(\pm c,0)$—foci, always located on the major axis

Although the derivation was long, sketching should be short.

EXAMPLE 4   Sketch $x^2/7 + y^2/5 = 1$

In the case of the ellipse, the longer axis is indicated by the larger number under x^2 or y^2. Try not to remember a or b. Remember the picture! This is longer in the x-direction. $y = 0$, major vertices

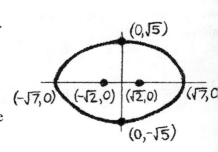

$(\pm 7^{1/2},0)$, $x = 0$, minor vertices $(0,\pm 5^{1/2})$. $c = (7-5)^{1/2}$. The foci are $(\pm 2^{1/2}, 0)$.

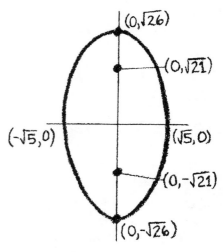

EXAMPLE 5 $x^2/5 + y^2/26 = 1$

Longer in the y direction. Major vertices $(0,\pm 26^{1/2})$. Minor vertices $(0,\pm 5^{1/2})$. $c = (26-5)^{1/2}$. Foci $(0,\pm 21^{1/2})$. Foci always on longer axis.

EXAMPLE 6 $(x-6)^2/7 + (y+4)^2/5 = 1$

This is the same basic example as number 4 except the middle is no longer at $(0,0)$. It is at the point $(6,-4)$. Major vertices $(6 \pm 7^{1/2},-4)$. Minor vertices $(6,-4 \pm 5^{1/2})$. Foci $(6 \pm 2^{1/2},-4)$.

Note: The numbers found in Example 4 are added and subtracted from the appropriate coordinate of the center $(6,-4)$. Also note that weird numbers were purposely chosen so that you could see where the numbers came from.

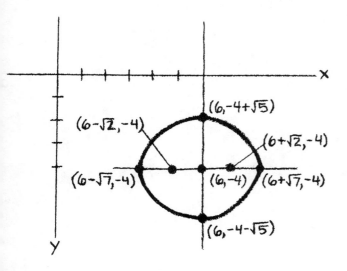

EXAMPLE 7 Sketch and discuss $4x^2 + 5y^2 + 30y - 40x + 45 = 0$.

Like the parabola and circle, we must complete the square, only a little differently.

$$4x^2 + 5y^2 + 30y - 40x + 45 = 0$$

Group the x and y terms; number to the other side

$$4x^2 - 40x + 5y^2 + 30y = -45$$

Factor out coefficients of x^2 and y^2; complete the square in the parenthesis; add the number term inside the parenthesis multiplied by the number outside the parenthesis to each side— with both x and y. Then do arithmetic and divide by 100 to get 1 on the right

$$4\left(x^2 - 10x + (-10/2)^2\right) + 5\left(y^2 + 6y + (6/2)^2\right) = -45 + 4(-10/2)^2 + 5(6/2)^2$$

$$4(x-5)^2/100 + 5(y+3)^2/100 = 100/100$$

or $\quad (x-5)^2/25 + (y+3)^2/20 = 1$

Center $(5,-3)$. Under the $(x-5)^2$ term is larger and $25^{1/2}$ to the left and right of the center. Major vertices $(5 \pm 25^{1/2}, -3)$. Under the $(y+3)^2$, $20^{1/2}$ above and below the center. Minor vertices $(5, -3 \pm 20^{1/2})$. $c = (25-20)^{1/2}$. Foci, on larger axis, $(5 \pm 5^{1/2}, -3)$.

Of course you should put 5 instead of $25^{1/2}$, but I left $25^{1/2}$ to show you where 5 came from.

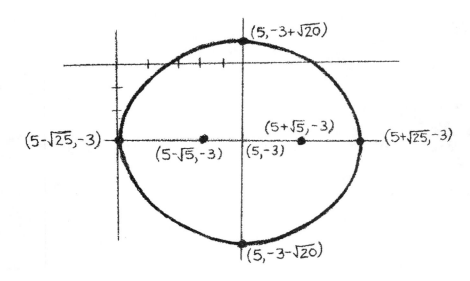

Definition HYPERBOLA — Set of all points P such that $F_1P - PF_2 = 2a$. The derivation is exactly the same as the ellipse. Once is enough!!!!! Equation is $x^2/a^2 - y^2/b^2 = 1$, where $a^2 + b^2 = c^2$. $(\pm a, 0)$—transverse vertices. $(\pm c, 0)$—foci. Asymptotes $y = \pm(b/a)x$. Slopes of the lines are square root of the number under the y^2 term over the square root of the number under the x^2 term. The shape of the curve depends on the location of the minus sign, *not* the largeness of the numbers under the x^2 or y^2 term.

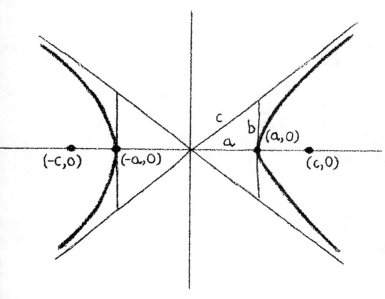

EXAMPLE 8 Sketch and label $x^2/7 - y^2/11 = 1$.

Transverse vertices $y = 0$ (set the letter after the minus sign equal to zero). $(\pm 7^{1/2}, 0)$. $c = (7 + 11)^{1/2}$. Foci $(\pm 18^{1/2}, 0)$. Asymptotes $y = \pm(11^{1/2}/7^{1/2})x$. **Note:** Curve does not hit y-axis. If $x = 0$, $y = \pm(-11)^{1/2}$, which are imaginary.

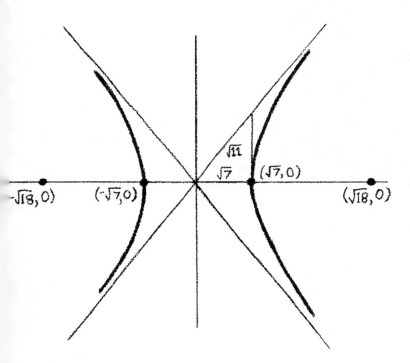

EXAMPLE 9 Sketch and discuss $y^2/5 - x^2/9 = 1$.

Let $x = 0$. Transverse vertices are $(0, \pm 5^{1/2})$. $c = (5 + 9)^{1/2}$. Foci are $(0, \pm 14^{1/2})$. Asymptotes $y = \pm(5^{1/2}/9^{1/2})x$. The sketch is as shown here.

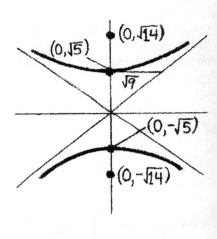

EXAMPLE 10 Sketch and discuss $(y - 6)^2/5 - (x + 7)^2/9 = 1$.

This is the same as example 9 except the "center" of the hyperbola, where the asymptotes cross, is no longer at $(0,0)$. The center is $(-7,6)$. $(x + 7)^2 = 0$; then $a = 5^{1/2}$, $5^{1/2}$ above and below the center. $c = (5 + 9)^{1/2}$. The foci are $14^{1/2}$ above and below the center. $V(-7, 6 \pm 5^{1/2})$. $F(-7, 6 \pm 14^{1/2})$. Asymptotes $y - 6 = \pm(5^{1/2}/9^{1/2})(x + 7)$.

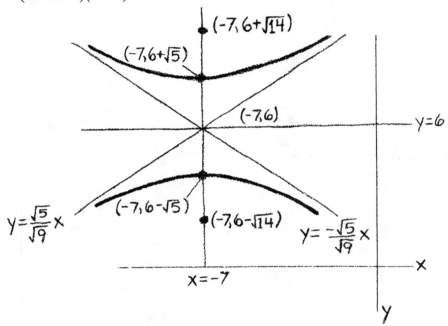

EXAMPLE 11 Sketch and discuss $25x^2 - 4y^2 + 50x - 12y + 116 = 0$.

For the last time, we will complete the square, again a little differently than the other times. We will use exactly the same steps as for the ellipse, except for the minus sign.

$$25x^2 - 4y^2 + 50x - 12y + 116 = 0$$

$$25x^2 + 50x - 4y^2 - 12y = -116$$

$$25[x^2 + 2x + (2/2)^2] - 4[y^2 + 3y + (3/2)^2] = -116 + 25(2/2)^2 - 4(3/2)^2$$

$$\frac{25(x + 1)^2}{-100} - \frac{4(y + 3/2)^2}{-100} = \frac{-100}{-100}$$

$$(y + 3/2)^2/25 - (x + 1)^2/4 = 1$$

Center $(-1,-3/2)$. $V(-1,-3/2 \pm 25^{1/2})$. $F(-1,-3/2 \pm 29^{1/2})$.
Asymptotes $y + 3/2 = \pm(25^{1/2}/4^{1/2})(x+1)$.

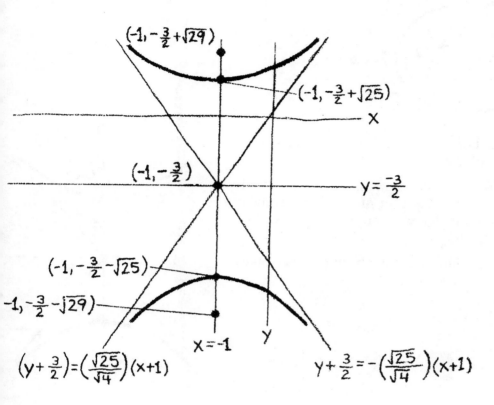

Sometimes we have a puzzle. Given some information can we find the equation? You must always draw the picture and relate the picture to its equation.

EXAMPLE 12 Find the equation of the parabola with focus $(1,3)$, directrix $x = 11$.

Drawing F and the directrix, the picture must be the one shown here. Vertex is half way between the x numbers. So $x = (11 + 1)/2 = 6$. $V(6,3)$. c = the distance between V and F = 5. The equation is $(y - 3)^2 = -4c(x - 6) = -20(x - 6)$. Remember the minus sign is from the shape and c is always positive for these problems.

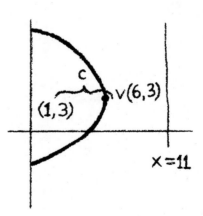

EXAMPLE 13 Vertices $(2,3)$ and $(12,3)$ and 1 focus $(11,3)$. Find the equation of the ellipse.

Two vertices give the center $\left((12 + 2)/2, 3\right) = (7,3)$. $F(11,3)$.
$(x - 7)^2/a^2 + (y - 3)^2/b^2 = 1$. $a = 12 - 7 = 5$. $c = 11 - 7 = 4$. $a^2 - b^2 = c^2$. $5^2 - b^2 = 4^2$. $b^2 = 9$ (no need for b). $(x - 7)^2/25 + (y - 3)^2/9 = 1$.

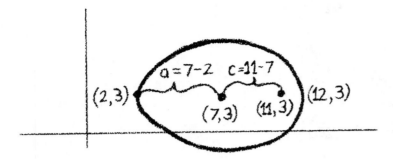

EXAMPLE 14 Find the equation of the hyperbola with vertices $(0,\pm 6)$ and asymptotes $y = \pm (3/2)x$.

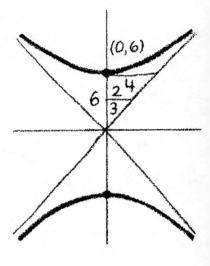

$V(0,\pm 6)$ says the center is $(0,0)$ and the shape is $y^2/36 - x^2/a^2 = 1$. The slope of the asymptotes is $3/2 = $ sq. root of the number under y^2 over the sq. root of the number under x^2 term. So $3/2 = 6/a$. So $a = 4$. So $a^2 = 4^2 = 16$. The equation is $y^2/36 - x^2/16 = 1$.

This kind of question is shorter in length, but it does take practice. So practice!!!

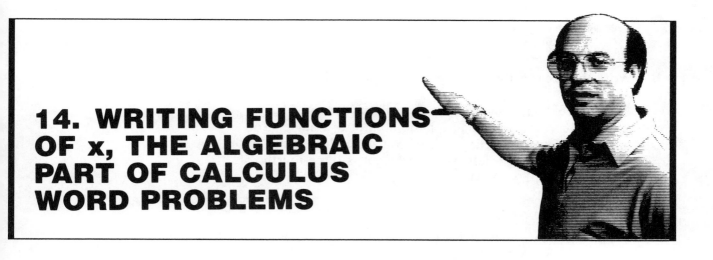

14. WRITING FUNCTIONS OF x, THE ALGEBRAIC PART OF CALCULUS WORD PROBLEMS

In calc I, the most difficult section for the most number of people is the section on word problems. It has very little to do with the calculus part of the problem. Ninety percent of the time the calculus is very, very easy. It is the algebraic setting up of the problem that causes all the problems. Most textbooks thoroughly neglect this area of algebra, and even if the book does have these problems, most of the time the teacher skips this section. In calculus you are then faced with both the algebra and calculus, which is too much for most students. We will try to make word problems a lot less painful.

Here are the keys to the word problems:

1. Don't panic.

2. Don't panic!

3. Don't panic!!!! These first 3 rules are very important.

4. Find out what you are solving for. This seems like a silly thing to say, but there is usually more than 1 possibility in the problem.

5. If there is a picture, draw it. On the picture label the unknowns in terms of 1 variable, if possible, or 2 variables otherwise.

6. If you have trouble with these problems, do not worry about it. Equally important, do not quit. Read the solutions over and over. With hard work, you will get the knack of doing these problems.

Let us start with an easy one.

EXAMPLE 1   If the height of a triangle is three-fourths of the base,

a.   Write the area of the triangle in terms of the base.

b. Write the area of the triangle in terms of the height.

In this problem, a picture is not really necessary. This problem tells you you are looking for the area of a triangle. You must know these formulas. They are, of course, earlier in this book. $A = \frac{1}{2}bh$. The problem also tells you the height is three-fourths of the base. In symbols, $h = (3/4)b$.

a. $A = \frac{1}{2}bh = \frac{1}{2}b[(3/4)b] = (3/8)b^2$

b. For this part, we must get b in terms of h. $h = (3/4)b$. $4h = 3b$. $b = (4/3)h$. So $A = \frac{1}{2}bh = \frac{1}{2}[(4/3)h]h = (2/3)h^2$.

OK. This one isn't too bad. Let's try another not too bad problem.

EXAMPLE 2 A farmer wishes to make a small rectangular garden with 1 side against the barn. If the farmer has 200 feet of fencing, find the expression for the area of the garden.

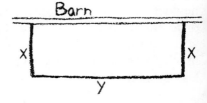

First we make what I used to call my crummy little diagram before a real publisher got it. The picture has to be just good enough to see what is going on. A ruler is advisable.

From the problem, we get that we are looking for the area. We draw the picture and label the sides. The trick, if you can call it a trick, is that the fencing does not include the side of the barn.

So $2x + y = 200$. So $y = 200 - 2x$. The area $A = xy$. But $y = 200 - 2x$. The expression for the area in terms of x is $A = x(200 - 2x)$ or $200x - 2x^2$.

So far so good. Let's try another one, one not quite so nice.

EXAMPLE 3 A potato farmer has a rectangular plot of land of 800 square feet. The 3 equal regions are pictured here.

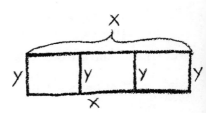

a. Find an equation for the length of fencing.

b. The outside fencing costs $20 a foot, while the inside is $7 a foot. Find an equation for the total cost.

a. The area $A = 800 = xy$. The fencing $f = 2x + 4y$. From the area equation, $y = 800/x$. So $f = 2x + 4y$ can be rewritten $f = 2x + 4(800/x)$. $f = 2x + 3200x^{-1}$.

b. The total cost is cost per foot times the number of feet. Outside fencing is $20 per foot. The number of feet is $2x + 2y = 2x + 2(800/x)$. Inside fencing is $7 per foot. The number of feet is $2y = 2(800/x)$. Total cost is $20[2x + 2(800/x)] + 7(2)(800/x) = 40x + 43,200x^{-1}$.

EXAMPLE 4   An open box with a square bottom is to be cut from a piece of cardboard 10 feet by 10 feet by cutting out the corners and folding the sides up. Find the volume of the box.

We must cut squares out of the corners, dimension x by x. The pictures of the formation of the box are here.

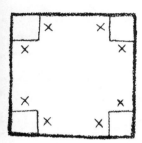 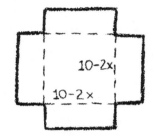 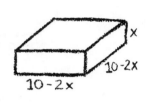

If the side is 10 and an x is cut off either end, the length and width are both $10 - 2x$. The height is x. $V = LWH = (10 - 2x)(10 - 2x)x$ or $4x^3 - 40x^2 + 100x$.

This one isn't too bad. The next one is a standard problem found in nearly all calc books.

EXAMPLE 5   A box has a square base and no top.

 a. Find an expression for the surface area if the volume is 80.

 b. Find an expression for the volume if the surface area is 50.

Let the base be of dimensions x by x, and the height is y. The picture is as shown here.

The volume is easy. $V = LWH = x^2y$. There are 5 sides for the surface area. The bottom is a square. Its area is x^2. The front, back, and 2 sides are all rectangles with the same dimensions x and y. The total surface area is $x^2 + 4xy$.

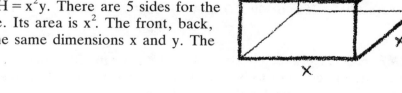

 a. $V = 80 = x^2y$. So $y = 80/x^2$.
    $SA = x^2 + 4xy = x^2 + 4x(80/x^2)$ or $x^2 + 320x^{-1}$.

 b. $SA = 50 = x^2 + 4xy$. $y = (50 - x^2)/4x$.
    $V = x^2y = x^2(50 - x^2)/4x = (25x)/2 - x^3/4$.

EXAMPLE 6   A 10-foot string is cut into 2 parts; 1 part is shaped into a circle and the other into a square. Find a formula that will give the sum of the areas.

Cut the string to make 1 piece x feet long. The remaining piece is $10 - x$ feet. The picture will look as shown here.

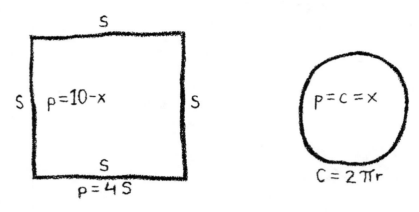

The circumference of the circle $c = x = 2\pi r$. So $r = x/2\pi$. Area of the circle $= \pi(x/2\pi)^2 = x^2/4\pi$.

The perimeter of the square $p = 10 - x = 4s$. So $s = (10 - x)/4$.

The area of the square is $s^2 = [(10 - x)/4]^2 = (x^2 - 20x + 100)/4$.

The total area is $x^2/4\pi + (x^2 - 20x + 100)/4$.

Not too nice. Remember to keep plugging. Notice this is one of the first answers with a pi in the denominator.

EXAMPLE 7   An orchard has 50 apple trees. The average number of apples per tree is 990. For each additional tree planted, the entire orchard gives 15 less apples per tree. Give an expression for the total number of apples.

The total number of apples = the number of trees times the apples per tree. If we add x trees, the total number of trees is $50 + x$. We lose 15 apples for each additional tree (or $-15x$). The number of apples per tree is $990 - 15x$. The total number of apples is $(50 + x)(990 - 15x)$ or $49,500 + 240x - 15x^2$.

EXAMPLE 8   A printer is using a broad page with 108 square inches. The margins are to be 1 inch on 3 sides and $\frac{1}{2}$ inch at the top. Find an expression for the printed area.

Page area $A = xy = 108$; so $y = 108/x$. Length is x. With 2 inches cut off, the length of the print is $x - 2$. Width of print is $y - 1.5$, $1\frac{1}{2}$ inches cut off.

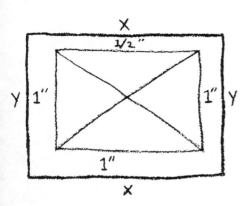

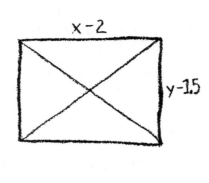

Area of the print is $(x-2)(y-1.5) = (x-2)(108x^{-1} - 1.5)$ or $-1.5x + 111 + 216x^{-1}$.

EXAMPLE 9   Find the distance between the graph $y^2 = 2x$ and the point $(2,0)$.

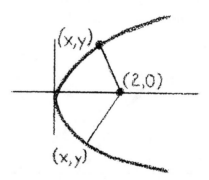

Distance means distance formula between the point (x,y) and $(2,0)$. $d = [(x-2)^2 + (y-0)^2]^{1/2} = (x^2 - 4x + 4 + y^2)^{1/2}$. But since $y^2 = 2x$, we can rewrite the distance formula $d = (x^2 - 4x + 4 + 2x)^{1/2}$ or $(x^2 - 2x + 4)^{1/2}$.

Note: A trick we will use in calculus is to use the square of the distance formula in order to avoid using the square root.

Here's another example that is found in most calc books.

EXAMPLE 10   A rectangle is inscribed in a parabola, $y = 12 - x^2$, with 2 vertices on the x-axis and 2 vertices on the parabola. Find the expressions for the area and the perimeter of the rectangle in 1 variable, as usual.

When we draw the picture, the rectangle must be symmetric with respect to the y-axis.

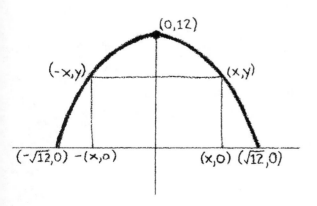

If (x,y) is any point on the curve, its symmetric point is $(-x,y)$. The base of the rectangle is $x - (-x) = 2x$ and the height is $y - 0 = y$.

The area $A = 2xy$. The perimeter is $4x + 2y$. However, since (x,y) is on the parabola, $y = 12 - x^2$. So $A = 2xy = 2x(12 - x^2)$ or $-2x^3 + 24x$.

$$p = 4x + 2y = 4x + 2(12 - x^2) \text{ or } -2x^2 + 4x + 24.$$

Hopefully these problems are now getting a little faster.

EXAMPLE 11   A rectangle is to be inscribed in a 6-8-10 right triangle, so that the sides of the rectangle are parallel to the legs and 1 vertex lies on the hypotenuse. Find the equation of the area of this triangle, in 1 variable.

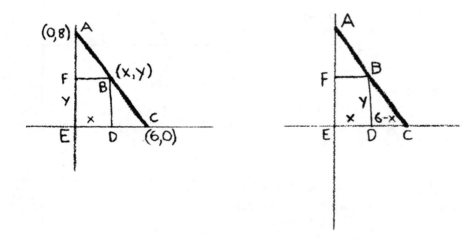

There are 3 things we note about this problem:

1.   We must set up the triangle in terms of the x-y axis, with the legs 6 and 8 on the x- and y-axes; it does not matter which leg is on which axis.

2.   Wherever point B is, it represents a point (x,y) on the hypotenuse. The area of the rectangle is xy.

3.   In order to find a relationship between x and y, we must see that triangles BCD and ACE are similar. (It is also possible to use triangle ABF.) Since $EC = 6$ and $ED = x$, $DC = 6 - x$. The proportion we get is

$$\frac{BD}{DC} = \frac{AE}{EC} \qquad \text{or} \qquad \frac{y}{6-x} = \frac{8}{6}$$

Solving for y (by cross multiplication) we get

$$y = \frac{8(6-x)}{6} \text{ or } 8 - 4x/3$$

So $A = xy = x(8 - 4x/3)$ or $-4x^2/3 + 8x$.

We now start a number of rather nasty problems.

EXAMPLE 12 Joan lives in an old house with a window that is in the shape of a rectangle surmounted with a semicircle. If its perimeter is 10 meters, find the area of the window. The picture is as shown here.

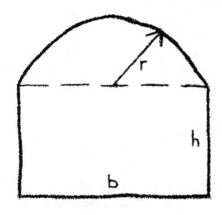

First, I don't know why they always say "surmounted," but they do. Next, there is a small trick to cut down on the fractions in this problem. We let $b = 4x$!!!!! We let $h = y$. Then $r = \frac{1}{2}b = 2x$.

The perimeter is 3 sides of a rectangle (not the dotted side) plus a semicircle.

$$p = 2h + b + \frac{2\pi r}{2} = 2y + 4x + \pi(2x) = 10 \quad \text{so} \quad y = 5 - 2x - \pi x$$

$$A = bh + \tfrac{1}{2}\pi r^2 = 4xy + \tfrac{1}{2}\pi(2x)^2 = 4x(5 - 2x - \pi x) + 2\pi x^2$$

$$= -2\pi x^2 - 8x^2 + 20x$$

They do not get any nicer.

However, you should be exposed to these kinds of problems now, and most calculus professors do not give them.

EXAMPLE 13 Write an equation for the volume of a cone inscribed in a sphere of radius 8. It must be in 1 variable, and the cone must touch the sphere in all possible places.

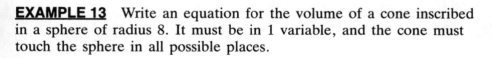

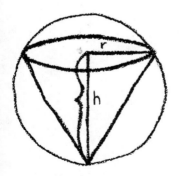 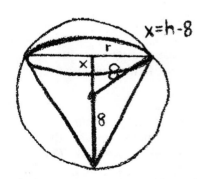

Again we note the symmetry of the cone inside the sphere. We see in the second picture here that we can find a relationship between r, x $(= h - 8)$, and the radius of the sphere 8. Old Pythagoras tells us $(h - 8)^2 + r^2 = 8^2$. $r^2 = 16h - h^2$. The volume of a cone $V = (1/3)\pi r^2 h = (1/3)\pi(16h - h^2)h$.

The reason we substitute for r^2 and not for h is that the calculus problem associated with this problem is *much* easier this way.

EXAMPLE 14   A man is on an island which is 4 miles from a straight shore. He wishes to go to a house which is 12 miles down the shore from the point that is the closest one to the island. Let x be the point where he lands on the shore. If he rows at 3 miles per hour and runs at 5 miles per hour, find the expression for the time it takes to get to the house.

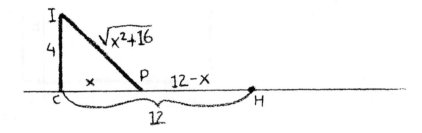

The island I is 4 miles from the closest point C on the shore. We label as point P the point the man would row to. So $CP = x$. Then $PH = 12 - x$. IP is the Pythagorean theorem $(x^2 + 16)^{1/2}$.

I call this problem the ultimate rate × time = distance problem. We are looking for time = distance/rate.

	Distance	Rate	Time = Distance/Rate
From I to P (in the water)	$(x^2 + 16)^{1/2}$	3	$(x^2 + 16)^{1/2}/3$
From P to H (on land)	$12 - x$	5	$(12 - x)/5$

Total time $t = \dfrac{(x^2 + 16)^{1/2}}{3} + \dfrac{12}{5} - \dfrac{x}{5}$

The calculus part of this problem is not particularly nice either, although, as usual, it is the translation of the verbal problem into algebra that causes problems.

There is 1 more problem we will do 2 ways: 1 using only algebra and 1 involving trig, as some of the problems in calculus do. The setting up, the part we will do here, should be studied. The calculus part is probably the nicest part, although it is not nice. The algebraic simplification is very messy. The trig simplification is really clever.

EXAMPLE 15   A fence is 8 feet tall and is on level ground. The fence is parallel to a high building and is 1 foot from the building. A ladder over the fence touches the ground and the building. Find an expression for the length of the ladder.

Note: If this seems like a strange problem, the calculus problem is to find the smallest ladder to do the trick.

Note: The picture is usually given. However, you do have to assign the variable x. The picture is as shown here.

Algebraic solution:

We are looking for the length of the ladder, AE. We let AB = x. From the problem, BC = 1. By Pythagoras, $AD = (x^2 + 64)^{1/2}$. We have similar traingles ABD and ACE.

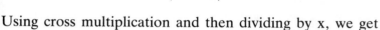

$$\frac{AB}{AD} = \frac{AC}{AE} \quad \text{or} \quad \frac{x}{(x^2 + 64)^{1/2}} = \frac{x+1}{AE}$$

Using cross multiplication and then dividing by x, we get

$$\text{length of ladder } AE = \frac{(x+1)(x^2 + 64)^{1/2}}{x}$$

Trig solution:

We will do the problem in terms of the angle at A.

$$\cot A = AB/8 = x/8 \qquad x = 8 \cot A$$

In writing trig functions, always try to get the unknown in the numerator. It makes calculations easier

$AB = x = 8 \cot A \qquad AC = AB + 1 = 8 \cot A + 1$

$\sec A = \text{length of ladder}/AC = AE/AC \qquad$ so

$AC \sec A = \text{length of ladder}$

The length of the ladder is $(8 \cot A + 1) \sec A = 8 \csc A + \sec A$ since $(\cot A)(\sec A) = (\cos A/\sin A)(1/\cos A) = 1/\sin A = \csc A$. (You must know those identities.)

If you work really hard on these problems, when you get to calculus you will be surprised how easy they will become.

15. THE BINOMIAL THEOREM

Unless something else comes up, this is the last topic. We would like to find the multiplied-out expression for, let us say, $(x + y)^8$, without saying $(x + y)$ times $(x + y)$, getting the answer, multiplying again by $(x + y)$, and so on. This would take a very long time to do. There are a number of ways to find the expression. I think this method, looking at the pattern of each term, is the best.

$$(x + y)^n = x^n + \frac{n}{1} x^{n-1}y^1 + \frac{n(n-1)}{1(2)} x^{n-2}y^2 + \frac{n(n-1)(n-2)}{1(2)(3)} x^{n-3}y^3$$
$$+ \frac{n(n-1)(n-2)(n-3)}{1(2)(3)(4)} x^{n-4}y^4 + \cdots$$

Do you see the pattern? If you do you are pretty darn good. However, a numerical example will help.

EXAMPLE 1   Using the binomial theorem, write out and simplify all terms of $(2a - b)^5$. This takes a lot of space.

$$(2a - b)^5 = (2a)^5 + \frac{5}{1} (2a)^4(-b)^1 + \frac{5(4)}{1(2)} (2a)^3(-b)^2$$
$$+ \frac{5(4)(3)}{1(2)(3)} (2a)^2(-b)^3 + \frac{5(4)(3)(2)}{1(2)(3)(4)} (2a)^1(-b)^4$$
$$+ \frac{5(4)(3)(2)(1)}{(1)(2)(3)(4)(5)} (2a)^0(-b)^5$$

We must make lots of observations.

1. If the power is n, n a positive integer, there are $n + 1$ terms. In Example 1 the power is 5; the number of terms is 6.

2. If there is a minus sign, the *even* terms are negative (second, fourth, sixth . . .).

100

3. Although we will not show it, it is possible for n to be a fraction or negative. In that case, we would get an infinite number of terms.

4. Notice the pattern of each term. For example, the fifth term in Example 1: The power of the second letter is 4, 1 less than the number of the term; 4 is the number of terms top and bottom in the coefficient; the bottom always starts at 1 and goes up to the power of the second term, in this case 4; the top starts at the power and goes down, and the number of terms is again the power of the second term, in this case 4 $(5 \times 4 \times 3 \times 2)$; the powers of the letters add up to n, in this case 5—we have b^4, so a is to the 1st power; in the fifth term—odd number—the sign is plus.

Let us do another problem using the observations in item 4.

EXAMPLE 2   Given $(3a - 5b)^{10}$. Write the fourth term only and simplify.

Well, we could write out all 4 terms, but that is a pain.

1. The sign is negative since it is the fourth term (even).

2. Since it is the fourth term, it contains $(5b)^3$.

3. Three is the number of terms on the bottom of the fraction: $1 \times 2 \times 3$.

4. Three on the bottom, 3 on the top starting with 10: $10 \times 9 \times 8$.

5. Power of $(5b)$ is 3. The total powers must add to 10. Soooooooo the power of $(3a)$ is 7.

The whole term is

$$-\frac{(10)(9)(8)}{(1)(2)(3)} (3a)^7 (5b)^3 \quad \text{or} \quad -120(3a)^7(5b)^3$$

The coefficient of a^7b^3 is 120 times 3^7 times 5^3. (Don't forget the coefficient part of each letter.) The whole answer is $-32,805,000a^7b^3$.

Note: The coefficient part of the term, in this case, $10(9)(8)/(1)(2)(3)$, is always an integer. You should cancel first before you multiply.

Also note: If you are asked for a term in which the first letter has the smaller exponent, use that number in writing the numerical coefficient.

One more example—a little trickier.

EXAMPLE 3 $[x^2 + (1/x)]^6$. Write the term that contains no x.

We must write out 2 terms to see the pattern:

$$(x^2)^6 + (6/1)(x^2)^5(1/x)^1 + \cdots = x^{12} + 6x^9 + \cdots$$

The exponents go down by 3. So we are looking for the fifth term. It contains $(1/x)^4$. On the bottom of the fraction is 1 times 2 times 3 times 4. On the top of the fraction is 6 times 5 times 4 times 3 (4 terms starting with 6 and going down). Since $(1/x)$ is to the 4th and $4 + 2 = 6$, x^2 must be to the 2nd power—$(x^2)^2$. So the term is

$$\frac{(6)(5)(4)(3)}{(1)(2)(3)(4)} (x^2)^2(1/x)^4 = 15x^4(1/x^4) = 15$$

Unless I can think of anything else, this is the end. I hope you found this book useful. If you have any comments, corrections, or additions, write me. I hope you will go on to use my CALC I and CALC II HELPERS.

ACKNOWLEDGMENTS

I have many people to thank.

I would like to thank my wife Marlene who makes life worth living.

I thank the two most wonderful children in the world, Sheryl and Eric for being themselves.

I would like to thank my brother Jerry for all his encouragement and for arranging to have my non-professional editions printed.

I would like to thank Bernice Rothstein of the City College of New York and Sy Solomon at Middlesex County Community College book stores for allowing my books to be sold in their book stores and for their kindness and encouragement.

I would like to thank Dr. Robert Urbanski, chairman of the math department at Middlesex, first for his encouragement, and secondly for recommending my books to his students because the students found the books valuable.

I thank Bill Summers of the CCNY audio-visual department for his help on this and other endeavors.

Next I would like to thank the backbone of three schools, their secretaries: Hazel Spencer of Miami of Ohio, Libby Alam and Efua Tongé of the City College of New York, and Sharon Nelson of Rutgers.

I would like to thank Marty Levine of MARKET SOURCE for first presenting my books to McGraw-Hill.

I would like to thank McGraw-Hill, especially John Carleo, John Aliano, David Beckwith and Pat Koch. Hopefully this will be the beginning of a long and mutually beneficial relationship.

I would also like to thank my parents, Lee and Cele, who saw the beginnings of these books but did not live to see their publication.

Lastly I would like to thank three people who helped keep my spirits up when things looked very bleak: a great friend, Gary Pitkofsky, another terrific friend and fellow lecturer, David Schwinger, and my sharer of dreams, my cousin, Keith Ellis, who also did not live to see my books published.

INDEX

Absolute value, 17
   equations, 18
   inequalities, 18
Amplitude, 44
Angle:
   degrees, 39
   radians, 39
   related, 42
   revolutions, 39
Angle of depression, 62
Angle of elevation, 62
Arc length, 23
Asymptotes:
   horizontal, 69
   hyperbola, 87
   oblique, 70, 73
   vertical, 68
Axix of symmetry, 26
Binomial theorem, 100
Box:
   diagonal, 22
   surface area, 22
   volume, 22
   word problem, 93
Circle:
   area, 22
   chord, 23
   circumference, 23
   diameter, 23
   equation of, 25
   radius, 23
   secant, 23
   sector, 23
   tangent, 23
   word problem, 94
Complement, 24

Completing the square:
   circle, 25
   ellipse, 85
   hyperbola, 88
   parabola, 82
   quadratic formula, 8
Complex fraction, 20
Composite function, 35
Cone:
   volume, 23
   word problem, 97
Cosecant, 40
Cosine, 40, 43
Cosines, law of, 64
Cotangent, 40
Cube:
   diagonal, 22
   surface area, 22
   volume, 22
Curve sketching:
   polynomials, 65
   rational functions, 68
Cylinder:
   surface area, 23
   volume, 23
Degree of polynomial, 68
Directrix, parabola, 81
Distance:
   formula, 25
   word problem, 95, 98
Domain, 28, 37, 38
Ellipse:
   co-vertices, 84
   foci, 83
   major axis, 84
   major vertices, 84

   minor axis, 84
   minor vertices, 84
Equations:
   absolute value, 18
   circle, 25
   ellipse, 83, 84, 89
   hyperbola, 86, 90
   line, 5, 6
   parabola, 26, 81, 89
   quadratic, 7
   trig, 50, 58
Exponents:
   fractional, 19, 75
   negative, 19
Focus:
   ellipse, 83
   hyperbola, 87
   parabola, 81
Function, 28
   composite, 35
   domain, 28, 37, 38
   inverse, 36
   inverse trig, 59
   notation, 28
   one to one, 31
   range, 28, 37, 38
   slope of secant line, 30
   word problems, 91–99
Graphs, drawing:
   absolute value, 32
   in pieces, 33, 34
   line, 3, 31
   parabola, 27, 32
   semi-circle, 33
   square root, 33
Half-life, 79

Hyperbola:
    asymptotes, 86
    equation, 86
    foci, 86
    vertices, 86
Identities, trig, 47–50,
    54–59
Inequalities:
    absolute value, 18
    linear, 11
    quadratic, 12
Intercepts:
    line, 3
    parabola, 26
    polynomial, 65
Interest, 79
Inverse functions, 36
Inverse trig functions, 59
Line:
    equation, 5, 6
    graph, 3, 31
    horizontal, 4
    point-siope, 4
    slope-intercept, 4
    standard form, 1
    vertical, 4
Linear inequalities, 11
Logs, 75–78
    half life, 79

    interest, 79
    one-to-one, 77
Midpoint, 25
One-to-one:
    functions, 31
    logs, 77
Parabola:
    axis of symmetry, 26
    equation, 26, 81, 89
    vertex, 26, 81
    word problem, 95
Period, 43
Point-slope, 4
Pythagorean theorem, 24
    word problems, 98, 99
Quadratics:
    equation, 7
    formula, 8, 52
    inequalities, 12–16
Range, 28, 37, 38
Rectangle:
    area, 22
    diagonal, 22
    perimeter, 22
    word problems, 92, 94, 96
Right triangle, 24
Secant, 23, 31, 40
Sector, 23
Sine, 40, 43

Sines, law of, 62
Slope, line, 1, 2
Slope-intercept, 4
Square:
    area, 22
    diagonal, 22
    perimeter, 22
    word problems, 94
Standard form, line, 1
Supplement, 24
Tangent, 40, 43
Trapezoid, 23
Transverse vertices, 86
Triangle inequality, 17
Triangles:
    area, 23
    equilateral, 24
    isosceles, 24
    perimeter, 23
    right triangle, 24
    word problems, 96
    30°-60°-90°, 24, 41
    45°-45°-90°, 24, 41
Trig equations, 50–53
Trig functions:
    domain, 53
    range, 53
Trig right triangle, 61
Vertex, parabola, 26, 81

MY NOTES

MY NOTES

MY NOTES

MY NOTES

MY NOTES

MY NOTES

SCHAUM'S INTERACTIVE OUTLINE SERIES

Schaum's Outlines and Mathcad™ Combined. . .
The Ultimate Solution.

NOW AVAILABLE! Electronic, interactive versions of engineering titles from the Schaum's Outline Series:

- *Electric Circuits*
- *Electromagnetics*
- *Feedback and Control Systems*
- *Thermodynamics For Engineers*
- *Fluid Mechanics and Hydraulics*

McGraw-Hill has joined with MathSoft, Inc., makers of Mathcad, the world's leading technical calculation software, to offer you interactive versions of popular engineering titles from the Schaum's Outline Series. Designed for students, educators, and technical professionals, the *Interactive Outlines* provide comprehensive on-screen access to theory and approximately 100 representative solved problems. Hyperlinked cross-references and an electronic search feature make it easy to find related topics. In each electronic outline, you will find all related text, diagrams and equations for a particular solved problem together on your computer screen. Every number, formula and graph is interactive, allowing you to easily experiment with the problem parameters, or adapt a problem to solve related problems. The *Interactive Outline* does all the calculating, graphing and unit analysis for you.

These "live" *Interactive Outlines* are designed to help you learn the subject matter and gain a more complete, more intuitive understanding of the concepts underlying the problems. They make your problem solving easier, with power to quickly do a wide range of technical calculations. All the formulas needed to solve the problem appear in real math notation, and use Mathcad's wide range of built in functions, units, and graphing features. This interactive format should make learning the subject matter easier, more effective and even fun.

For more information about *Schaum's Interactive Outlines* listed above and other titles in the series, please contact:

Schaum Division
McGraw-Hill, Inc.
1221 Avenue of the Americas
New York, New York 10020
Phone: 1-800-338-3987

To place an order, please mail the coupon below to the above address or call the 800 number.

--✄ ---

Schaum's Interactive Outline Series
using Mathcad®

(Software requires 80386/80486 PC or compatibles, with Windows 3.1 or higher, 4 MB of RAM, 4 MB of hard disk space, and 3 1/2" disk drive.)

AUTHOR/TITLE	Interactive Software Only ($29.95 ea)		Software and Printed Outline ($38.95 ea)	
	ISBN	Quantity Ordered	ISBN	Quantity Ordered
MathSoft, Inc./DiStefano: Feedback & Control Systems	07-842708-8	_____	07-842709-6	_____
MathSoft, Inc./Edminister: Electric Circuits	07-842710-x	_____	07-842711-8	_____
MathSoft, Inc./Edminister: Electromagnetics	07-842712-6	_____	07-842713-4	_____
MathSoft, Inc./Giles: Fluid Mechanics & Hydraulics	07-842714-2	_____	07-842715-0	_____
MathSoft, Inc./Potter: Thermodynamics For Engineers	07-842716-9	_____	07-842717-7	_____

NAME_____ADDRESS_____

CITY _____ STATE_____ZIP_____

ENCLOSED IS   ❑ A CHECK ❑ MASTERCARD   ❑ VISA ❑ AMEX   (✓ ONE)

ACCOUNT #_____EXP. DATE _____

SIGNATURE_____

MAKE CHECKS PAYABLE TO McGRAW-HILL, INC. PLEASE INCLUDE LOCAL SALES TAX AND $1.25 SHIPPING/HANDLING

Schaum's Outlines and Solved Problems Books
in the
BIOLOGICAL SCIENCES

SCHAUM OFFERS IN SOLVED-PROBLEM AND QUESTION-AND-ANSWER FORMAT THESE UNBEATABLE TOOLS FOR SELF-IMPROVEMENT.

❈ Fried **BIOLOGY** ORDER CODE 022401-3/$12.95
(including 888 solved problems)

❈ Jessop **ZOOLOGY** ORDER CODE 032551-0/$13.95
(including 1050 solved problems)

❈ Kuchel et al. **BIOCHEMISTRY** order code 035579-7/$13.95
(including 830 solved problems)

❈ Meislich et al. **ORGANIC CHEMISTRY, 2/ed** ORDER CODE 041458-0/$13.95
(including 1806 solved problems)

❈ Stansfield **GENETICS, 3/ed** ORDER CODE 060877-6/$12.95
(including 209 solved problems)

❈ Van de Graaff/Rhees **HUMAN ANATOMY AND PHYSIOLOGY** ORDER CODE 066884-1/$12.95
(including 1470 solved problems)

❈ Bernstein **3000 SOLVED PROBLEMS IN BIOLOGY** ORDER CODE 005022-8/$16.95

❈ Meislich et al. **3000 SOLVED PROBLEMS IN ORGANIC CHEMISTRY** ORDER CODE 056424-8/$22.95

Each book teaches the subject thoroughly through Schaum's pioneering solved-problem format and can be used as a supplement to any textbook. If you want to excel in any of these subjects, these books will help and they belong on your shelf.

Schaum's Outlines have been used by more than 25,000,000 student's worldwide!

PLEASE ASK FOR THEM AT YOUR LOCAL BOOKSTORE OR USE THE COUPON BELOW TO ORDER.

ORDER CODE	TITLE	QUANTITY	$ AMOUNT
_____	_____	_____	_____
_____	_____	_____	_____
_____	_____	_____	_____
		LOCAL SALES TAX	_____
		$1.25 SHIPPING/HANDLING	_____
		TOTAL	_____

NAME _____
(please print)

ADDRESS _____
(no P.O. boxes please)

CITY _____ STATE _____ ZIP _____

ENCLOSED IS ❑ A CHECK ❑ MASTERCARD ❑ VISA ❑ AMEX (✓ one)

ACCOUNT # _____ EXP. DATE _____

SIGNATURE _____

MAIL PAYMENT AND COUPON TO:

MCGRAW-HILL, INC.
ORDER PROCESSING S-1
PRINCETON ROAD
HIGHTSTOWN, NJ 08520
OR CALL
1-800-338-3987

MAKE CHECKS PAYABLE TO MCGRAW-HILL, INC. PRICES SUBJECT TO CHANGE WITHOUT NOTICE AND MAY VARY OUTSIDE U.S. FOR THIS INFORMATION, WRITE TO THE ADDRESS ABOVE OR CALL THE **800** NUMBER.

SCHAUM'S SOLVED PROBLEMS SERIES

- Learn the best strategies for solving tough problems in step-by-step detail
- Prepare effectively for exams and save time in doing homework problems
- Use the indexes to quickly locate the types of problems you need the most help solving
- Save these books for reference in other courses and even for your professional library

To order, please check the appropriate box(es) and complete the following coupon.

- ❑ **3000 SOLVED PROBLEMS IN BIOLOGY**
  ORDER CODE 005022-8/**$16.95** **406 pp.**

- ❑ **3000 SOLVED PROBLEMS IN CALCULUS**
  ORDER CODE 041523-4/**$19.95** **442 pp.**

- ❑ **3000 SOLVED PROBLEMS IN CHEMISTRY**
  ORDER CODE 023684-4/**$20.95** **624 pp.**

- ❑ **2500 SOLVED PROBLEMS IN COLLEGE ALGEBRA & TRIGONOMETRY**
  ORDER CODE 055373-4/**$14.95** **608 pp.**

- ❑ **2500 SOLVED PROBLEMS IN DIFFERENTIAL EQUATIONS**
  ORDER CODE 007979-x/**$19.95** **448 pp.**

- ❑ **2000 SOLVED PROBLEMS IN DISCRETE MATHEMATICS**
  ORDER CODE 038031-7/**$16.95** **412 pp.**

- ❑ **3000 SOLVED PROBLEMS IN ELECTRIC CIRCUITS**
  ORDER CODE 045936-3/**$21.95** **746 pp.**

- ❑ **2000 SOLVED PROBLEMS IN ELECTROMAGNETICS**
  ORDER CODE 045902-9/**$18.95** **480 pp.**

- ❑ **2000 SOLVED PROBLEMS IN ELECTRONICS**
  ORDER CODE 010284-8/**$19.95** **640 pp.**

- ❑ **2500 SOLVED PROBLEMS IN FLUID MECHANICS & HYDRAULICS**
  ORDER CODE 019784-9/**$21.95** **800 pp.**

- ❑ **1000 SOLVED PROBLEMS IN HEAT TRANSFER**
  ORDER CODE 050204-8/**$19.95** **750 pp.**

- ❑ **3000 SOLVED PROBLEMS IN LINEAR ALGEBRA**
  ORDER CODE 038023-6/**$19.95** **750 pp.**

- ❑ **2000 SOLVED PROBLEMS IN Mechanical Engineering THERMODYNAMICS**
  ORDER CODE 037863-0/**$19.95** **406 pp.**

- ❑ **2000 SOLVED PROBLEMS IN NUMERICAL ANALYSIS**
  ORDER CODE 055233-9/**$20.95** **704 pp.**

- ❑ **3000 SOLVED PROBLEMS IN ORGANIC CHEMISTRY**
  ORDER CODE 056424-8/**$22.95** **688 pp.**

- ❑ **2000 SOLVED PROBLEMS IN PHYSICAL CHEMISTRY**
  ORDER CODE 041716-4/**$21.95** **448 pp.**

- ❑ **3000 SOLVED PROBLEMS IN PHYSICS**
  ORDER CODE 025734-5/**$20.95** **752 pp.**

- ❑ **3000 SOLVED PROBLEMS IN PRECALCULUS**
  ORDER CODE 055365-3/**$16.95** **385 pp.**

- ❑ **800 SOLVED PROBLEMS IN VECTOR MECHANICS FOR ENGINEERS**
  Vol I: STATICS
  ORDER CODE 056582-1/**$20.95** **800 pp.**

- ❑ **700 SOLVED PROBLEMS IN VECTOR MECHANICS FOR ENGINEERS**
  Vol II: DYNAMICS
  ORDER CODE 056687-9/**$20.95** **672 pp.**

ASK FOR THE *SCHAUM'S* SOLVED PROBLEMS SERIES AT YOUR LOCAL BOOKSTORE OR CHECK THE APPROPRIATE BOX(ES) ON THE PRECEDING PAGE AND MAIL WITH THIS COUPON TO:

McGRAW-HILL, INC.
ORDER PROCESSING S-1
PRINCETON ROAD
HIGHTSTOWN, NJ 08520

OR CALL
1-800-338-3987

NAME   (PLEASE PRINT LEGIBLY OR TYPE)

ADDRESS   (NO P.O. BOXES)

CITY   STATE   ZIP

ENCLOSED IS   ❒ A CHECK   ❒ MASTERCARD   ❒ VISA   ❒ AMEX   (✓ ONE)

ACCOUNT # _____   EXP. DATE _____

SIGNATURE _____

MAKE CHECKS PAYABLE TO MCGRAW-HILL, INC. <u>PLEASE INCLUDE LOCAL SALES TAX AND **$1.25** SHIPPING/HANDLING</u>
PRICES SUBJECT TO CHANGE WITHOUT NOTICE AND MAY VARY OUTSIDE THE U.S.   FOR THIS
INFORMATION, WRITE TO THE ADDRESS ABOVE OR CALL THE **800** NUMBER.